CHEMISTRY

Lab Manual
Teacher's Edition
for use with Third Edition

Verne Biddle

Brad R. Batdorf

Lynne Woodhull

BJU PRESS

Greenville, South Carolina

PLEASE NOTE:

You are legally responsible for the safety of your students in the lab. Insist that they follow safe lab practices. Do not leave them unattended while they are working on any experiment or project in the lab.

The law requires that all permanent containers (not beakers, flasks, etc., that are used only during experiments) be labeled with an HMIS (Hazardous Materials Identification System) label. HMIS labels rank the chemical hazard in terms of health, flammability, reactivity, and contact on a scale from 0 to 4 (0 = no hazard; 4 = extreme hazard). The information you will need to prepare these labels can be found in the MSDS (Material Safety Data Sheet) obtained from the chemical supplier. These are available online if you do not have a copy of one you need.

An MSDS must be on file for each chemical you have on hand, and it must be located in an area that is easily accessible to your students. It would be a valuable use of your instructional time to go over the HMIS/MSDS formats with your students. In fact, they will be using one to answer questions in Laboratory Exercise 1.

Your legal responsibilities as a laboratory instructor are covered for the most part by the following groups of regulations:

1. Occupational Safety and Health Standards, especially OSHA 29 CFR 1910.1200 Hazard Communication and OSHA 29 CFR 1910.1450 Occupational Exposure to Hazardous Chemicals in Laboratories.

2. EPA Summary of Small Quantity Hazardous Waste Generator Rules—Resource Conservation and Recovery Act (40 CFR 261.5).

An excellent book that explains these regulations in plain English is *Investigating Safely: A Guide for High School Teachers* by Julian Texley, Terry Kwan, and John Summers (2004, NSTA Press).

You may want to consult your school lawyer to determine whether any local or state regulations should be taken into consideration. Rules regarding laboratory safety and chemical disposal are constantly changing. Safety and disposal procedures in this lab manual should be regarded as only generalized suggestions. You should consult the safety and chemical disposal laws in your own state and community, as well as the most recent OSHA guidelines.

Although you may resent the intrusion of the government into your classroom, your example will influence the attitude of your students with regard to personal safety, a Christian's responsibility to government, and our responsibility for the environment.

NOTE: The fact that materials produced by other publishers may be referred to in this volume does not constitute an endorsement of the content or theological position of materials produced by such publishers. Any references and ancillary materials are listed as an aid to the student or the teacher and in an attempt to maintain the accepted academic standards of the publishing industry.

CHEMISTRY Laboratory Manual Teacher's Edition
For use with Third Edition

Authors
Verne Biddle, PhD
Brad R. Batdorf, MA Ed
Lynne Woodhull

Project Editor
Adelé Hensley

Project Manager
Franklin Hall

Page Design
Carol Jenkins
Dan VanLeeuwen

Cover Design
Aaron Dickey

Illustration
Amber Cheadle
John Cunningham

Formerly published as *Laboratory Manual: CHEMISTRY FOR CHRISTIAN SCHOOLS Teacher's Edition*.

Produced in cooperation with the Bob Jones University Division of Natural Science of the College of Arts and Science.

© 2009 BJU Press
Greenville, South Carolina 29614

First Edition © 1985, 1993 BJU Press
Second Edition © 2000 BJU Press

Printed in the United States of America

ISBN 978-1-5911-772-8

15 14 13 12 11 10 9 8 7 6 5 4 3 2 1

OUR COMMITMENT.
YOUR SATISFACTION.

CREATIVE

Updated, colorful pages.
Exciting activity ideas.

COMPLETE

Overprint answers, teaching tips,
and supplementary information.

CHRISTIAN

Nothing to conflict with Truth.
Everything to support it.

Contents

Introduction

Chemistry is an experimental science based on observation. While performing experiments from this laboratory manual, you will make qualitative and quantitative observations. Qualitative observations use words to describe things, while quantitative observations use numbers to describe specific amounts. These observations lead to inquiry and problem solving. The experiments in this laboratory manual incorporate one or more of the following tasks involved in problem solving: *planning and designing, performance, analysis and interpretation,* and *application.*

The task of planning and designing involves formulating questions, predicting results, or designing an experimental procedure. This laboratory manual uses all three of these aspects of planning and designing to some degree. For example, it offers several special, unstructured exercises without the traditional fill-in-the-blank laboratory reports. In these exercises, you will design your own procedure and write your own laboratory report.

The task of performance includes manipulating material, making decisions and observations, and recording data. All of the experiments in this manual provide these opportunities. In an introductory chemistry course such as this, the performance tasks are limited in order to emphasize various laboratory techniques and standard equipment. The limitation of tasks also ensures greater safety.

The analysis task involves processing data, explaining relationships, arriving at generalizations, and discussing accuracy. Some of the exercises designed with step-by-step procedures are written so that you perform them before you are introduced to the text material. The other step-by-step exercises follow the text material to emphasize it. Both types offer you the opportunity to analyze data.

In the application step of problem solving, you formulate a hypothesis based on your experimental results and make predictions for new situations.

This laboratory manual is divided into several sections. First, the manual has a table of contents that allows you to find laboratory exercises quickly and easily. The major section, the experimental section, follows the introduction to the manual and contains laboratory experiments that are organized by chapter to correlate with material covered in *Chemistry*, Third Edition. At the back of this manual are appendixes on data interpretation, laboratory equipment, and laboratory techniques, followed by a list of safety rules, which are arranged in categories for fast and easy reference.

This laboratory manual also has an organized structure within each experiment. Each experiment will have four areas. The **Prelab** section contains the goals for the experiment and an introduction that relates the experiment to the textbook. *Checkup* questions follow the introduction to test your understanding of the general concepts and procedures. Also, the Prelab section lists the materials that you will need for the experiment. Beneath this list of materials are some safety icons that alert you to possible hazards. A key to these icons appears on this page. The **Procedure** section follows the Prelab and gives step-by-step instructions on how you should perform the experiment. The **Data** section provides a place for you to record all of your observations. These may be qualitative

Safety Icons

Body protection
Chemicals, stains, or other materials could damage your skin or clothing. You should wear a laboratory apron or gloves or both.

Chemical fumes
Chemical fumes may present a danger. Use a chemical fume hood or make sure the area is well ventilated.

Electricity
An electrical device (hot plate, lamp, microscope) will be used. Use the device with care.

Extreme temperature
Extremely hot or cold temperatures may cause skin damage. Use proper tools to handle laboratory equipment.

Eye protection
There is a possible danger to the eyes from chemicals or other materials. Wear safety goggles.

Fire
A heat source or open flame is to be used. Be careful to avoid skin burns and the ignition of combustible materials.

Gas
Improper use of gas can result in burns, explosion, or suffocation. Be careful to check that the gas is turned off when you are finished.

Poison
A substance in the investigation could be poisonous if ingested.

Sharp objects
Cuts are possible from broken glassware (broken test tubes, thermometers, microscope slides) or sharp instruments.

You will find additional teaching tips and lists of materials and chemicals in the back of this Teacher's Edition.

For the remainder of the lab manual, TE marginal notes will be placed in this font. Whenever possible, the note will be in the margin directly adjacent to the paragraph to which it applies.

The minimum expectation of college professors for students is the knowledge of introductory techniques and standard equipment. Go over the names of laboratory equipment frequently.

The laboratory reports that the students write for the special experiments should follow this outline of four sections.

Nitrile gloves can be obtained through science suppliers and should be available for students when needed. With reasonable care, they can be reused several times.

or quantitative. Finally, an **Analysis** section contains questions for you to answer and calculations for you to perform.

Working with chemicals sometimes involves certain hazards, such as fire, toxicity, and skin irritation. However, hazards can be minimized by following directions, heeding cautions, and wearing protective equipment, such as goggles and aprons, when necessary. Note the safety icons for each lab to determine the needed protection. In addition to an apron and goggles, it may be wise to wear latex or nitrile gloves to protect your hands for some of the labs. The nitrile type is recommended due to an increasing incidence of allergic reactions to latex. Working in the laboratory safely is an important skill that you should be learning and practicing during this course. A safe laboratory environment is everyone's responsibility, so be informed!

Suppliers of hazardous materials provide Material Safety Data Sheets (MSDS) to accompany their products. These sheets inform the user of the specific hazards involved, the properties of the material, first aid to be administered, protective equipment to be used, waste disposal, and so on. They will be available for immediate reference in the laboratory at all times.

1 Laboratory Introduction

Prelab

Concepts

This exercise will help you become familiar with several aspects of the laboratory: the equipment, the rules, the techniques, and the role of the observer. You should see not only the importance of making accurate observations in a science class but also how everyone's observations are prone to bias.

Usually, reading the experiment and answering the Checkup questions is all that is required before class, but this exercise is an exception. In addition to your routine prelab assignment, you should read the list of Laboratory Techniques (Appendix C) and the Laboratory Safety and First-Aid Rules (Appendix D). In class you will complete the Analysis section and fill in a Check-In Form using the diagrams from the Laboratory Equipment section (Appendix B). These diagrams will help you identify the pieces of equipment.

Checkup

The answers to these questions must be written in ink and completed prior to class. You may not consult with anyone else.

1. What is the best thing to do if you spill a chemical on yourself?

   Flush the area with lots of water.

2. What is the first thing to do if a person swallows a chemical?

   Find out the specific substance ingested and contact the poison

   control center in your area immediately.

3. What is the purpose of the needle valve on a Bunsen burner?

   It is for adjusting the flame. It is *not* for turning off the burner.

4. What should you do if a Bunsen burner "strikes back"?

   Turn off the gas at the desk valve; then turn it back on and

   relight the burner.

5. Does a laboratory balance determine mass or weight? Are mass and weight quantitative or qualitative data? (See Section 1.15 in your textbook.)

   A laboratory balance compares an object to a standard; hence,

   it measures mass; quantitative data.

6. Without consulting with anyone else, describe the following four characteristics of your chemistry teacher from memory: eye color, hair color, approximate height, and clothing worn yesterday.

   Answers will vary.

Goals

✓ Learn to read a Material Safety Data Sheet (MSDS).

✓ Use a balance.

✓ Adjust a Bunsen burner.

✓ Make scientific observations.

Materials

assorted objects to observe and describe

balance

Bunsen burner

desk equipment (see check-in list)

graduated cylinder containing water

MSDS

Mass is compared to a standard, so it does not change. Weight is the measure of the pull of gravity, and it changes when gravity changes, such as in different parts of the world or universe.

Some suggestions for objects and substances to observe and describe would include the following:

- containers (vials) of mineral oil—viscous, colorless, liquid, faint odor

- sand—granular, tan, solid

- broken glass pieces—colorless, jagged, solid, fragile, with a chemical composition similar to sand but with different physical properties

- metal shot (copper, zinc, or lead)—solid, spherical or irregular shape, colored, dense

- para- or *p*-dichlorobenzene—white, solid, crystalline, "mothball" odor

- sulfur—yellow, solid or powder, possible faint disagreeable odor

- several clean iron nails—quantitative data, grayish, solid, dense

- iron (III) oxide—reddish brown, solid, powder

- oxygen gas or air—colorless, gas, low density

The objects and substances can illustrate the difference between the properties of free elements and their compounds in preparation for the next chapter.

Procedure

1. Refer to Appendix B, Laboratory Equipment, to help you identify each item on the Check-In Form.

2. Replace any equipment that is chipped or broken.

3. Turn in any equipment that is not on the Check-In Form.

4. Find the locations of all the safety equipment (eyewash, fire extinguisher, shower). Refer to Appendix D, Laboratory Safety and First-Aid Rules, to become familiar with ways to prevent injuries and to deal with any accidents that may occur.

5. Light your Bunsen burner. Refer to Appendix C, Laboratory Techniques. Note what happens to the flame when you rotate the barrel and the needle valve. *Do not rotate either one any more than you are instructed!* Record your observations by answering Questions 1–4 in the Analysis section.

6. Weigh on the balance the graduated cylinder containing the water. Answer Questions 5–6 in the Analysis section.

7. Examine the MSDS you have received and answer Questions 7–15 in the Analysis section.

8. Examine the items your teacher has available for you and record your observations in Analysis Question 16.

9. Answer Analysis Questions 17–18.

Analysis

1. Describe clearly what happens to the appearance of the flame as you rotate the *barrel* clockwise and counterclockwise. Be as descriptive as possible. _____

_____

2. Describe clearly what happens to the appearance of the flame as you rotate the *needle valve* clockwise and counterclockwise. Be as descriptive as possible. _____

_____

_____

3. Can you confidently say anything about the temperature of the flame at the various points of adjustment? If so, what? If not, what would be necessary to do so? _A thermometer or other measuring device is necessary_ _to say anything about the temperature of the flame. The observations are qualitative and would need a_ _calibrated instrument to make them quantitative._

_____

4. Are the descriptions you have given quantitative or qualitative? _qualitative_

5. To what decimal place does your balance permit you to record the mass of the graduated cylinder of water?

_____

6. Would you be able to determine only the mass of the water that is in the graduated cylinder? or only the volume? Explain your answers clearly. <u>There are two ways to determine the mass of the water. If you know the</u>
   <u>density of water ($D = M/V$), you could calculate the mass based on the volume. A more exact way would be</u>
   <u>to find the mass of the empty graduated cylinder first, and then subtract that amount from the cylinder</u>
   <u>containing the water.</u>

7. Give the product name for the chemical whose MSDS you have. _____

8. List any synonyms for this substance (a maximum of three). _____
   _____

9. What is the percentage composition of this substance? _____
   _____

10. List the potential effect(s) this chemical will have for each of the following types of exposure:
    eye contact _____
    skin contact _____
    inhalation _____
    ingestion _____

11. What first aid is recommended for each kind of exposure?
    eye contact _____
    skin contact _____
    inhalation _____
    ingestion _____

12. What personal protection is recommended? _____

13. What are its physical properties? (Write *n/a* if no information is given.)
    melting point _____
    boiling point _____
    solubility in water _____
    color _____

14. Is your chemical stable? _____

15. Is it designated as being incompatible with any specific substances? If so, with what?
    _____

The following questions must be answered as individuals, not as partners.

16. On the following blanks, list the items your teacher has provided for you to observe, followed by as much description as possible (include properties such as color, state, shape, odor, and appearance). Circle any descriptions that are quantitative.
    _____
    _____
    _____
    _____

17. Is bias involved in any of your observations and descriptions in Question 16? Which? Explain.

    Odor should be at least one of the listed items that involve bias.

18. How did your observations concerning your teacher in Question 6 of the Checkup compare with reality? Were any of them prone to bias? Explain.

    Height and clothing may be subject to the bias of the observer. For example, someone who is short

    would think another person is tall when he actually may be of average height, but the same person would

    be perceived as short to someone who is tall; style of clothing is very subject to the taste or bias of the

    individual.

Data

Check-In Form

Put a check mark beside each item that is in your drawer.

Desk Equipment		
Quantity	Description	Check-in
2	beakers, 150 mL and 250 mL	
1	Bunsen burner	
1	clay triangle	
1	crucible and cover	
1	crucible tongs	
1	Erlenmeyer flask, 250 mL	
1	evaporating dish	
3	eyedroppers or plastic transfer pipets	
1	filtering funnel, 55 mm (3–4 in.)	
	filter paper	
1	glass stirring rod	
1	goggles	
1	graduated cylinder, 10 mL	
1	iron ring	
1	laboratory apron	
	matches	
1	pinchcock clamp	
1	ring stand	
1	spatula	
1	test tube brush	
1	test tube clamp	
1	test tube holder	
1	test tube rack	
2	test tubes (large), 18 mm × 150 mm	
10	test tubes (small), 13 mm × 100 mm	
1	wash bottle	
2	watch glasses, 60 mm and 150 mm	
1	wire gauze	

✓ I have read the Laboratory Safety and First-Aid Rules and have located all the safety equipment in the laboratory. I further certify that my drawer or cabinet is fully stocked according to the above list.

Signature _____ Date _____

Emphasize that the students should keep their drawers or cabinets clean and completely stocked at all times.

You may want to keep a laboratory breakage list so that when items are broken, students can be charged.

If necessary, be sure to add or delete any items on this Check-In Form before the students begin this laboratory procedure.

2A Percentage of Mixtures

Prelab

Concepts

If a solvent can be found that dissolves only one of the substances in a mixture, then the components of that mixture can be separated. One of the most common substances used for this purpose is water. Water is sometimes referred to as the *universal solvent* because it dissolves so many substances. The undissolved substance can then be removed from the mixture with a filter, and the solvent can be boiled off from the solution that passes through the filter. The dissolved substance (the *solute*) is left as a separate solid.

Checkup

1. What solvent will you use in this lab to dissolve the salt in the mixture? <u>hot tap water</u>

2. Should you measure the amount of solvent you will add to the mixture? Why or why not?

   <u>No. The water is boiled off eventually, so the amount is not</u>
   <u>important.</u>

3. How will you separate the sand from the solution?

   <u>by filtering the sand from the solution</u>

4. How will you separate the solute from the solvent?

   <u>by boiling away the water, leaving the salt behind</u>

5. How will you calculate your percent recovery?

   <u>Add the percentage of salt recovered to the percentage of sand</u>
   <u>recovered. (You can calculate the salt or sand percentages by</u>
   <u>dividing the part by the whole.)</u>

Procedure

1. Wash and thoroughly dry a 150 mL beaker and an evaporating dish.
2. Find the mass of the beaker, the dish, and a piece of dry filter paper to the nearest 0.01 g. (Record: 1–3.)
3. Place between 1–2 g of a mixture of salt and sand in the 150 mL beaker.
4. Find the mass of the beaker and its contents to the nearest 0.01 g. (Record: 4.)

Goal

✓ Separate a mixture into its components by using filtering and evaporating techniques.

Materials

balance
beakers, 150 mL and 250 mL
Bunsen burner
clay triangle
crucible tongs
evaporating dish
filtering funnel
filter paper
graduated cylinder, 10 mL
iron ring
matches
ring stand
sand
sodium chloride (NaCl)
watch glass, 150 mm
wire gauze

Materials

Table salt is acceptable for all experiments requiring sodium chloride.

The command "Record" will follow any procedure when the student should go to the Data section and record something. Following this command will be the location in the Data section where the student should write the data. For example, "Record: 1" refers the student to the Data section, blank 1.

Prepare the mixture before the lab period. Measure out a 2 g sample as a reference so that the students can see approximately how much to take. To save time, you may instead wish to have tubes containing the approximate amounts available so that each group will have one.

5. Filter the sand from the mixture.

a. Fold and moisten a piece of filter paper. Press it against the funnel wall. (See Appendix C.)

b. Set the filtering funnel in a clay triangle on an iron ring. Lower the ring until the tip of the funnel stem touches the inside rim of the evaporating dish. (When the funnel stem touches another surface, it drains better; see Figure 2A-1.)

c. Empty your sample mixture from the beaker onto the filter paper. You may need to tap your beaker with a pen or pencil to dislodge any particles that adhere to the beaker.

d. Using your graduated cylinder, slowly pour four 5 mL portions of hot water from the tap over the mixture. Catch the filtrate in the evaporating dish. Allow each 5 mL portion to run through the mixture before adding the next portion. Pour the final 5 mL of water around the upper edge of the filter paper.

e. Remove the filtering funnel and the clay triangle and place the wire gauze on the iron ring in their place.

6. Evaporate the salt from the solution.

a. Place the evaporating dish containing the salt solution on the wire gauze and bring it to a *gentle* boil. Allow the salt water to simmer until most of the water has been boiled off and crystals begin to form in the dish. Do not heat so strongly that spattering occurs. Then carefully pick up the dish with the crucible tongs. Place an empty 250 mL beaker on the wire gauze and set the evaporating dish on top of it. (See Figure 2A-2.) Use this air bath to evaporate the solution to dryness. (The air bath reduces splattering and loss of crystals during the last stages of drying.)

2A-1 Filtering apparatus

b. While you are waiting for the salt solution to evaporate in Step 6a, carefully open the filter paper containing the sand onto a watch glass. Set the watch glass at the base of your burner. By the time your salt solution has evaporated, the sand and filter paper should also be dry. (If they are not dry by the time the solution has evaporated, leave them overnight and do Step 6c the next day.)

c. When the sand and paper appear to be dry, determine the mass to the nearest 0.01 g. (Record: 5.)

Instruct the students to be cautious. If even a small amount of water is present when the students apply direct heat, the sudden generation of steam will splatter large amounts of salt onto the watch glass. If this occurs, the students must wash the salt from the watch glass into the evaporating dish with water from an eyedropper and place it back onto the air bath for further evaporation.

d. When the evaporating dish appears to contain only dry salt (no hissing sound will be heard), cover it with a watch glass and again place it directly on the wire gauze.

e. After placing the evaporating dish on the wire gauze, heat it gently to dry the outside and to ensure that the salt is dry. If no splattering occurs, heat it strongly for about five minutes.

7. Allow the dish and contents to cool to room temperature on the wire gauze, and then determine the mass to the nearest 0.01 g. (Record: 6.)

2A-2 Air bath

Data

1. Mass of 150 mL beaker _____ g
2. Mass of evaporating dish _____ g
3. Mass of filter paper _____ g
4. Mass of beaker and mixture _____ g
5. Mass of filter paper and sand _____ g
6. Mass of evaporating dish and salt _____ g

Analysis

1. What was the mass of the mixture before the separation? _____ g
2. How much sand did you recover? _____ g
3. How much salt did you recover? _____ g
4. What is the percentage of sand in the mixture?

$$\left(\frac{\text{part}}{\text{total}} \times 100\% \right)$$ _____ %

5. What is the percentage of salt in the mixture?

$$\left(\frac{\text{part}}{\text{total}} \times 100\% \right)$$ _____ %

6. What is your total percent recovery? _____ %

Possible grading scale:

  A: 95–105% recovery

  B: 90–94% or 106–110% recovery

  C: 85–89% or 111–115% recovery

  D: Below 85% or above 115% recovery

If the sand or salt was not completely dry, the result will be greater than 100%.

2B Classification of Matter

Prelab

Concepts

Matter can be classified either as a pure substance or as a mixture. As shown in Figure 2B-1, both of these classifications of matter can be subdivided. **Pure substances** consist of only a single substance—an element or a compound—while **mixtures** are physical combinations of two or more substances. For example, iron (Fe) and iodine (I_2) are pure substances (elements). These pure substances can combine chemically to form the pure substance iron (II) iodide (a compound), or they can combine physically to form a granular mixture of solid iron and iodine (a heterogeneous mixture).

A mixture of iron and iodine has distinctly different characteristics from those of the compound iron (II) iodide. The most notable differences are the following: the proportions of iron and iodine are variable in the mixture but are fixed in the compound; the properties of the individual components are observable in the mixture but are not observable in the compound; and the components of the mixture can be separated by physical means, but physical methods alone cannot separate the iron and iodine in the compound.

In this laboratory exercise, you will observe the differences in the properties of iron filings, iodine crystals, a mixture of the iron filings and iodine crystals, and the compound iron (II) iodide. You will observe and record their physical appearance. Then, in a series of tests you will observe their magnetic behavior, their solubility in water, and their chemical activity, if any.

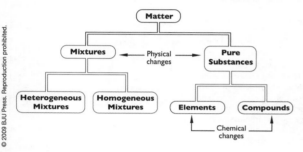

2B-1   The classification of matter

Goals

✓ Classify mixtures and compounds based on observed differences.

✓ Improve your ability to record and understand your observations.

Materials

ammonia solution (NH_3), dilute
balance
Bunsen burner
distilled water
evaporating dish, small
glass stirring rod
graduated cylinder, 10 mL
iodine (I_2) crystals
iron (Fe) filings
iron ring
magnet
magnifying glass
matches
ring stand
test tubes, 4
test tube holder
test tube rack
transfer pipet (or eyedropper)
weighing paper
wire gauze

Checkup

1. What two elements will be evaluated in this lab exercise?

   iron and iodine

2. What mixture will be evaluated?

   a mixture of iron filings and iodine crystals

3. What compound will be evaluated? ___iron (II) iodide___

4. How will you distinguish between a mixture and a compound?

   Answers will vary. The student should mention that the mixture

   and the compound should have different observable proper-

   ties, such as their physical appearances, their behavior in the

   presence of a magnetic field, water solubility, and chemical

   changes in the presence of the other element. Physical methods

   should be able to separate the elements of the mixture but not

   of the compound.

Procedure

1. Wear the safety clothing specified by your teacher.

2. Observe the physical appearances of the elements iodine and iron. Using the spatulas provided with each container, measure out on separate pieces of weighing paper 0.3 g of iodine crystals and 0.5 g of iron filings. (Caution! Do not touch the iodine crystals with unprotected skin or get them on your clothing. Iodine will cause stains! Gloves are recommended.) Describe the physical appearance of each element, especially noting any differences between them. Use a magnifying glass to aid your inspection. (Record: 1.)

3. Observe the magnetic behavior of the elements by passing a magnet under each sample. *Keep the weighing paper between the samples and the magnet* so that magnetic substances do not remain stuck to the magnet. (Record: 2.)

4. Observe the solubility of the elements.

   a. Place one or two crystals of iodine into one test tube and a few iron filings into a second test tube.

   b. Add about 20 drops of distilled water to each test tube with a transfer pipet. Agitate each tube for several minutes as demonstrated by your teacher and observe. Note any evidence of either element dissolving in the water. A chemical test for the presence of dissolved iron (II) ions (Fe^{2+}) is the appearance of a greenish solid precipitate in the presence of ammonia solution. Add a few drops of dilute ammonia solution (NH_3) to the test tube containing the iron filings. Does any of it dissolve? (Record: 3.)

5. Carefully pour the remainder of your sample of iodine crystals onto the weighing paper containing the iron filings and mix them with a *dry* stirring rod. Carefully describe the appearance of the mixture. (Record: 1.) Evaluate the magnetic behavior of the mixture as in Step 3. Note if the entire mixture responds to the magnet or only a part of the mixture. Be specific. (Record: 2.)

6. Carefully pour the mixture of iron filings and iodine into a clean test tube and add 5 mL of distilled water. Mix the contents of the tube with the stirring rod for several minutes, or until you see no further evidence of change. Pay particular attention to mixing the

You may need to grind the iodine crystals in a mortar with a pestle if they are not fine crystals. Sodium thiosulfate ($Na_2S_2O_3$) solution may be used to clean any iodine stains. Filings should be approximately 40 mesh.

solid at the bottom of the tube. Did you notice any absorption or liberation of heat? Record any evidence that a new substance was formed (e.g., color change, formation of a gas, different solid materials). Did you observe any change in the amount of iodine crystals or iron filings in the bottom of the test tube? (Record: 3.)

7. In this chemical change, the visual evidence for the production of a totally different material may not be conclusive. However, you can prove that the iron metal combined with iodine to form iron (II) iodide.

   a. Draw off 2–3 mL of the clear liquid from the test tube with a clean transfer pipet and add it to a small evaporating dish.

   b. Place the evaporating dish on a wire gauze supported by a ring clamped to a support stand. Gently heat the contents of the dish over low heat to prevent spattering. When the liquid is *almost* gone, remove the burner and allow the residual heat of the dish to completely dry the residue of iron (II) iodide. Record its appearance. (Record: 1.)

   c. After the evaporating dish has cooled, scrape the solid from the bottom of the dish with a spatula. Bring the magnet against the underside of the dish. Observe the response of the compound to a magnetic field. (Record: 2.)

   d. Transfer about 20 drops of the liquid from Step 6 to another clean test tube and add several drops of dilute ammonia solution to it. Does a precipitate form? Are Fe^{2+} ions present? What can you conclude about the solubility of the compound in water? (Record: 3.)

8. Clean up your glassware, put away equipment, and dispose of any waste as directed by your teacher.

Data

	Elements		Mixture	Compound
	Fe	I_2	$Fe + I_2$	FeI_2
1. Describe the appearance of each sample.	grayish to brownish, dull, solid (Descriptions will vary.)	purple black, somewhat shiny, crystalline solid (Descriptions will vary.)	particles of both iodine and iron seen, intermixed (Descriptions will vary.)	crystalline substance, gray, black, or red violet in color (Descriptions will vary.)
2. Did the sample exhibit magnetic behavior?	yes	no	Yes; the iron filings retained their magnetic character.	no
3. Was the sample soluble? Give the evidence for your conclusion.	No; no precipitate formed with NH_3 solution.	No (or slightly soluble); the crystals did not disappear, but the water did turn a brownish color.	The solubility of the mixture of Fe and I_2 cannot be determined because a reaction occurs as soon as water is added.	Yes; iodine crystals decreased in amount; a brownish red solution formed; evaporation showed that a new compound had formed with different properties; Fe^{2+} ions formed a greenish precipitate.

Analysis

1. From your magnified observation of physical appearance, could you tell whether the dry iron-iodine mixture was homogeneous or heterogeneous? If so, which was it? How could you tell?

   Yes; it was heterogeneous. Particles of iron and iodine crystals could be seen mixed together, and each retained its own physical appearance.

2. State in what ways the characteristics of the compound you formed differed from the elements composing it.

   It was completely soluble, but the elements were not or only slightly so. It had a different color. It was not magnetic.

3. Considering the definitions of compounds and mixtures, did you expect the compound to have properties that differed from the elements composing it? Why or why not?

   Yes; since compounds are chemical combinations of elements rather than physical mixtures, they usually have properties significantly different from those of the elements composing them.

4. How could a mixture of iron and iodine be separated into its elements? Would this work for the compound iron (II) iodide? Why or why not?

   A magnet could separate the iron metal from the iodine solid. (Not discussed in the lab is using an organic solvent which will dissolve the iodine but not the iron.) No; this would not work for iron (II) iodide since it is not magnetic and the elements are chemically combined, producing different properties for the compound as a whole. Separation of chemically combined elements requires chemical means, not physical means.

5. In Step 6, you were asked if the amount of iodine crystals changed as you observed the chemical change. Based on what you observed for iodine in Step 4, could any observed disappearance of iodine likely be caused by its dissolving? Why or why not?

   No. In Step 4, iodine crystals were found to be insoluble (or only slightly soluble), so their rapid disappearance noted in Step 6 would not likely be due to simple dissolution.

2B Classification of Matter (alternate)

Prelab

Concepts

Matter can be classified either as a pure substance or as a mixture. As shown in Figure 2B-1, both of these classifications of matter can be subdivided. **Pure substances** consist of only a single substance—an element or a compound—while **mixtures** are physical combinations of two or more substances. For example, iron (Fe) and sulfur (S) are pure substances (elements). These pure substances can combine chemically to form the pure substance iron (II) sulfide (a compound), or they can combine physically to form a granular mixture of solid iron and sulfur (a heterogeneous mixture).

A mixture of iron and sulfur has distinctly different characteristics from those of the compound iron (II) sulfide. The most notable differences are the following: the proportions of iron and sulfur are variable in the mixture but are fixed in the compound; the properties of the individual components are observable in the mixture but are not observable in the compound; and the components of the mixture can be separated by physical means, but physical methods alone cannot separate the iron and sulfur in the compound.

In this laboratory exercise, you will observe the differences in the properties of iron filings, sulfur powder, a mixture of iron filings and sulfur powder, and the compound iron (II) sulfide. You will observe and record their physical appearance. Then, in a series of tests you will observe their magnetic behavior, their solubility in water, and their chemical activity, if any, including combustibility.

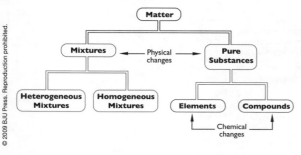

2B-1   The classification of matter

Goals

✓ Classify mixtures and compounds on the basis of observed differences.

✓ Improve your ability to record and understand your observations.

Materials

Bunsen burner
graduated cylinder, 10 mL
hydrochloric acid (HCl), 6 *M**
iron (Fe) filings
iron (II) sulfide (FeS)
iron and sulfur mixture
magnet
magnifying glass
matches
spatula
sulfur (S) powder or granules
test tubes, 4
test tube rack
weighing paper

*Corrosive: Avoid unprotected contact and do not breathe fumes.

Materials

Prepare the iron-sulfur mixture by grinding iron filings (approximately 40 mesh) and sulfur crystals with a mortar and pestle. Display small piles of each substance so that students will know how much to take.

Cut-up printer paper may be substituted for weighing papers.

Do NOT perform this lab unless your laboratory has operating fume hoods. Use Lab 2B instead.

Checkup

1. What two elements will be evaluated in this lab exercise?

   iron and sulfur

2. What mixture will be evaluated?

   a mixture of iron filings and sulfur powder

3. What compound will be evaluated in this exercise?

   iron (II) sulfide

4. How will you distinguish between a mixture and a compound?

   Answers will vary. The student should mention that the mixture

   and the compound should have different observable proper-

   ties, such as their physical appearances, their behavior in the

   presence of a magnetic field, water solubility, and chemical

   changes in the presence of the other element. Physical methods

   should be able to separate the elements of the mixture but not

   of the compound.

Procedure

1. Wear the safety clothing specified by your teacher.

2. Observe the physical appearance. Obtain pea-sized samples of iron, sulfur, the iron-sulfur mixture, and the compound iron (II) sulfide, and place them on separate pieces of weighing paper. Describe the physical appearance of each sample, noting any differences between them. Use a magnifying glass to aid your inspection. (Record: 1.)

3. Observe the magnetic behavior of the substances by passing a magnet under each sample. *Keep the weighing paper between the samples and the magnet* so that magnetic substances will not stick to the magnet. (Record: 2.)

4. Test for combustibility.

   a. Place approximately half of your iron sample on a spatula and insert it into the hottest part of the Bunsen burner flame for about 30 seconds. Look for evidence that the iron burned. Repeat this procedure in a fume hood for the other samples. (Record: 3a.)

   b. If any substance remains after the combustion test, place it on a clean piece of paper and test it with a magnet as in Step 3 above. (Record: 3b.)

5. Test for other chemical changes.

   a. Obtain 10 mL of 6 M HCl in your graduated cylinder. Divide it into nearly equal parts among the four test tubes.

   b. Drop the remainder of your iron sample into one test tube and observe whether a chemical change occurs (e.g., a color change occurs, a new substance forms, bubbles form). Repeat for the three other samples using a separate test tube for each. (Record: 4.)

   c. Pour the remaining acid solutions (HCl) into the designated acid waste container.

Deflagrating spoons may be used in Step 4a if you have them.

Burning sulfur releases noxious SO_2 gas. Make sure that students do not burn large samples.

Dissolving FeS may color the HCl solution yellow. Caution the class that *dissolving* is not necessarily the same thing as *reacting*.

Neutralize the collected acid waste by *cautiously* adding solid sodium carbonate to the waste until no more frothing occurs. Pour this neutralized solution down the drain diluted with plenty of running water.

Data

	Elements		Mixture	Compound
	Fe	**S**	**Fe + S**	**FeS**
1. What does each sample look like?	granular or filings, gray or rust brown color	fine, bright yellow powder	distinctly visible particles of iron mixed in and covered with sulfur powder	crystalline solid, may be white if pure or black if it contains impurities
2. Did the sample exhibit magnetic behavior?	yes	no	yes	slightly
3. a. Did the sample burn?	no	yes	yes	no
b. If a residue remained, was it magnetic?	yes	no	yes	slightly
4. Did the sample react with HCl?	yes	no	yes	yes

Analysis

1. From your magnified observation of physical appearance, could you tell whether the iron-sulfur mixture was homogeneous or heterogeneous? If so, which was it? How could you tell?

   Yes; it was heterogeneous. Particles of iron and sulfur powder could be seen mixed together; each retained its own physical appearance. The mixture was distinctly non-uniform based on a magnified inspection.

2. Would you make the same observation for the compound iron (II) sulfide? Why or why not?

   No; the heterogeneous mixture classification applies only to mixtures and not to compounds, which are pure substances and always homogeneous. Its properties were different from those of the elements composing it.

3. In Step 3, you indicated which substances displayed magnetic behavior. What happened to the magnetic properties of iron and sulfur when they were combined in a mixture? What happened when they were chemically combined in FeS?

   Iron and sulfur in the mixture had the same magnetic properties as isolated elements. In the compound FeS, however, it was expected that iron and sulfur would combine to make a compound with different magnetic properties, which was observed.

4. How could an iron-sulfur mixture be separated into its elements? Could this method extract elements from FeS?

   A magnet could pull the iron from the mixture. Sulfur in the mixture could be removed by burning. Not discussed in the lab is using the inorganic solvent carbon disulfide (CS_2), which will dissolve the sulfur but not the iron. None of these methods would break down iron (II) sulfide and separate it into its elements.

5. Iron melts at 1538 °C and sulfur melts at 115 °C. Does this information allow you to determine the melting point of iron (II) sulfide? Why or why not?

No; usually, properties of compounds are totally different from the properties of their elements. Students

may conclude that the FeS melting point would be somewhere in between these melting points.

(The actual melting point is approximately 1194 °C.)

3A Significant Digits in Measurements

Prelab

Concepts

Measurements are an important part of most science classes; they quantify matter so that we can have a better understanding of God's creation. Using and developing your skills of observation to describe matter qualitatively—as you did in Lab 2B—is important. However, it is also important to be able to describe matter quantitatively or measurably.

No measured quantity can ever be *exact*; there will always be some uncertainty associated with it. The degree of certainty in a measurement is reflected in the number of **significant digits** (often shortened to SDs) contained in it. The significant digits in a measurement contain all the certain digits—those of which we can be sure—and one uncertain digit. Just where that uncertainty lies depends on the measuring instrument.

Measuring instruments that have smaller divisions are more precise than those that have larger divisions; smaller divisions allow greater certainty in measurement. For example, a ruler that is calibrated in centimeters will allow certainty down to the whole number of centimeters, and tenths of centimeters will be estimated (but significant).

Calculations involving measurements must also reflect the proper degree of reliability, as determined by the uncertainties in the measuring instruments. We cannot somehow gain reliability or certainty in a crude measurement by performing a mathematical operation (addition, subtraction, multiplication, or division) on it. Hence, if the ruler is calibrated to tenths of centimeters, then the tenths place is certain, and the hundredths of centimeters is estimated (and significant).

In this exercise you will make a variety of measurements using several common measuring instruments, determine the number of significant digits in them, and perform several calculations, expressing your answers with the proper number of significant digits.

Checkup

1. Can a measurement be exact? Explain your answer.

   No, all measuring instruments are limited to a certain number
   of decimal places they can measure.

2. What is meant by the term *significant digits*?

   all of the certain digits, plus one uncertain digit

3. When calculating the average thickness of a penny, does the number of pennies in the stack influence the number of significant digits allowed? Why or why not?

   No, the number of pennies is an exact number, and it does not
   affect the number of significant digits allowed in a calculation
   involving measurements.

Goals

✓ Learn about uncertainties in measurement.

✓ Express measurements using the proper number of significant digits.

✓ Use significant digits properly in calculations.

✓ Become familiar with common laboratory measuring instruments for length, mass, and volume.

Materials

balance

calculator

graduated cylinder, 10 mL

metric ruler (or meter stick), clear plastic

pennies from various dates, 10

test tube

4. Assuming that the following numbers are all *measured* quantities that are given without units, calculate the answers and express them using the proper number of significant digits, rounding where needed.

a. 0.560 ÷ 20

0.560 ÷ 20 = 0.028 = 0.03 (1 SD)

b. 1.50 + 25.2 + 0.033

1.50 + 25.2 + 0.033 = 26.733 = 26.7 (1 decimal place)

c. 206.0 × 0.51

206.0 × 0.51 = 105.06 = 110 (2 SDs)

Procedure

1. Measure the thickness of one penny, being certain to include one estimated number in your measurement. Lay the transparent ruler over the edge of the penny that you are holding in your fingers, carefully aligning one side of the penny with one of the markings on the ruler. Note that each numbered division on a metric ruler is in centimeters, and thus each small division is a millimeter, or a tenth of a centimeter. (Record: 1.)

2. Repeat Step 1 for stacks of pennies containing 4, 7, and 10 pennies; be sure to obtain as many significant digits as are allowed for your ruler. (Record: 1.) As you measure the pennies, note if there is any observable variation in the thickness of each.

3. Carefully measure the length and width of the cover of your laboratory manual in units of centimeters. The first time, measure it as if there were no millimeter marking on the ruler; that is, estimate the tenths place of a centimeter in the measurement. (Record: 2.) The second time, use the millimeter markings to estimate the hundredths place. (Record: 2.)

4. Be sure you know how to use the balance in your laboratory before you perform this step. Find the individual masses of 5 of your pennies. Select pennies that have a variety of dates for this exercise—some newer and some older. Use significant digits properly in your recorded values. (Record: 3.)

5. Fill a test tube to the brim with water and carefully transfer all of it to your graduated cylinder. With your eye on the same level as the meniscus (see Appendix C, Laboratory Techniques), measure the volume of water that the test tube contained. Be sure to include one estimated number in your measurement. (Record: 4.) Repeat this measurement of the volume of the same test tube two more times, being careful to fill the test tube to the brim each time. (Record: 4.)

Data

1.

Number of pennies in a stack	1 coin	4 coins	7 coins	10 coins
Thickness	cm	cm	cm	cm

2.

	Nearest tenth	Nearest hundredth
Length of book	cm	cm
Width of book	cm	cm

3.

Mass of penny	g	g	g	g
Year of penny				

4.

Volume of water	mL	mL	mL

Analysis

1. Calculate the average thickness of one penny for each set of pennies, using significant digits properly.

Number of pennies in a stack	1 coin	4 coins	7 coins	10 coins
Average thickness	cm	cm	cm	cm

Answers will vary, but be sure they have the correct number of significant digits, either two or three. Answers should all be expressed to two decimal places.

2. Which of these numbers is the most representative value for the average thickness of a penny? Explain.

The number obtained with 10 pennies is the best. The more of the same objects you have, the more likely the average will be accurately representative, rather than representing more of the thinner or thicker pennies. In addition, it is easier to measure several pennies accurately than it is to measure a single penny—the degree of error is decreased.

3. Calculate the area of the cover of your laboratory manual; then calculate its perimeter. Record both the unrounded value and the value with the proper number of significant digits.

	Unrounded	Using proper significant digits
Area, using nearest tenth	cm²	cm²
Area, using nearest hundredth	cm²	cm²
Perimeter, using nearest tenth	cm	cm
Perimeter, using nearest hundredth	cm	cm

4. Which set of calculated quantities is closer to the actual or *exact* area and perimeter—those using the nearest tenth of a centimeter or those using the nearest hundredth? Explain.

The calculated quantities using the nearest hundredth of a centimeter are closer to the actual, unmeasurable, exact quantities because they use more precise measurements—measurements with more significant digits. We can have greater confidence that measurements and calculations are closer to the actual, exact value when there are more significant digits in them.

5. In what decimal place was there uncertainty in the masses of the pennies?

Assuming your balance reads 0.01 g, the uncertainty is in the hundredths place.

6. Do you notice any difference in the mass of a penny relative to the year it was minted? If so, what was it?

Yes. Pre-1982 pennies average about 3.0 g; post-1982 pennies average about 2.5 g. (Copper-clad zinc pennies were introduced in 1982.)

7. Calculate the average mass of a penny, expressing it with the proper number of significant digits. Is it possible for your average to be significantly different from that obtained by another group in your class? Explain.

Average mass of a penny _____ g

Yes. It could vary by tenths of a gram, depending on how many pre-1982 ("older") and post-1982 ("newer") pennies were in the set of 5 pennies.

8. Calculate the average volume of water contained in your test tube.

Average volume _____ mL

9. In what decimal place is the uncertainty (precision) in your measurement of the water?

Uncertainty will vary depending on the type of graduated cylinder you have, but the answer should be one decimal place more than the calibrations.

10. Do you think the average of three trials gives a more reliable (more accurate) value for the volume of the test tube than a single measurement? Why or why not?

Yes, an average is generally more reliable than a single measurement (assuming equal care is exercised in obtaining it) because errors tend to cancel out somewhat when making multiple measurements. The more often one repeats a measurement, the more confident he can be that it is accurate—close to the actual value.

3B Measurement of Matter

Prelab

Concepts

The physical property density is frequently used to help identify substances. **Density** is defined as the mass per unit of volume ($D = m/V$). In the metric system, density has the units g/mL or g/cm³ for liquids and solids and g/L for gases.

You can determine the density of regular objects (those with exact shapes) by dividing the mass of the object by a volume calculated from measurements of the object. You can determine the density of both regular and irregular objects by dividing the mass of the object by the amount of water it displaces (which is its volume). For example, if you want to find the density of an irregular object such as a rock, first determine its mass. Then determine its volume by filling a graduated cylinder to a known level and placing the rock in the cylinder. The difference between the new level and the original level is the volume displaced by the rock. In this experiment, you will determine the density of a regular object by both methods and the density of an irregular substance (metal shot) by the water displacement method.

Checkup

1. Name several items that would be considered regular objects.

   Answers will vary, but they may include a sphere, cube, or
   cylinder.

2. Name several items that would be considered irregular objects.

   Answers will vary, but they may include a rock, spoon, or
   beaker.

3. How do you determine the density of a regular object?

   Divide its mass by its volume (determined by calculations from
   measurements of the object).

4. How do you determine the density of an irregular object?

   Divide its mass by its volume (determined by water
   displacement).

5. If you determine the density of an object using both methods, will the object you use be regular or irregular?

   regular

Goals

✓ Measure length, volume, and mass.
✓ Determine the densities of regular and irregular solids.
✓ Determine the percent error of an experiment.

Materials

balance
graduated cylinder, 10 mL
metal cylinder or bar
metal shot, approximately 30 g
metric ruler

Materials

A metal bar can be used instead of a cylinder, but the procedures and calculations must be changed accordingly.

Zinc, lead, or copper shot is recommended.

mL = cc = cm³ = cubic centimeters

Procedure

1. Using a metric ruler (in cm), measure the length and diameter of a cylindrical object to two decimal places. If it is a bar, measure its length, width, and height. (Record: 1–3.)

2. Determine the mass of the regular object accurately to 0.01 g. (Record: 4.)

3. Fill your 10 mL graduated cylinder to about the 5 mL mark. Always read it to the nearest 0.1 mL. (Record: 5.)

4. Holding your graduated cylinder at a 45° angle, carefully slide the regular object down the side of the cylinder and measure the volume to one decimal place. (Record: 6.) Be sure the object is submerged. (If it is not, repeat Steps 3 and 4 with slightly more water in the cylinder.)

5. Weigh a 150 mL beaker to 0.01 g. (Record: 7.)

6. Add 25–30 grams of metal shot to the beaker and find the total mass. (Record: 8.)

7. Repeat Steps 3 and 4, using the metal shot in place of the regular object. (Record: 9–10.)

8. Show the setups for your calculations neatly in the margin.

Data

1. Length of object _____ cm

2. Diameter (or width) of object _____ cm

3. Height of bar _____ cm

4. Mass of regular object _____ g

5. Original volume of water in the graduated cylinder _____ mL

6. Final volume of water after the object was added _____ mL

7. Mass of 150 mL beaker _____ g

8. Mass of 150 mL beaker with metal shot _____ g

9. Original volume of water in the graduated cylinder _____ mL

10. Final volume of water and metal shot _____ mL

Analysis

Method 1: For Regular Objects

1. What is the radius of the regular object (cylinder only)? _____ cm
   ($r = d/2$)

2. What is the calculated volume of the object? _____ cm³
   $V = \pi r^2 h$ (cylinder) or $V = lwh$ (bar)

3. What is the density of the regular object ($D = m/V$)? _____ g/mL

Depending on the size of the shot that you use, you may need to have the students begin with more than 5 mL of water in their graduated cylinders; *all* the shot must be covered with water.

Since 1 mL of H_2O = 1 cm³ of H_2O = 1 g of H_2O, you can interchange the units mL, cm³, and g for water.

Method 2: For Regular and Irregular Objects

4. What is the volume of the regular object according to water displacement? _____ mL

5. What is the density of the regular object ($D = m/V$)? _____ g/mL

6. What is the *percent difference* of the two densities in Methods 1 and 2? _____ %

7. What is the volume of the metal shot according to water displacement? _____ mL

8. What is the density of the metal shot ($D = m/V$)? _____ g/mL

9. What is your *percent error* for the shot?
(Your teacher will give you the actual density of the metal shot.) _____ %

10. Which method do you think is more accurate for the regular object—direct measurement (Method 1) or displacement (Method 2)? Explain. <u>Water displacement is generally more accurate because slight imperfections</u>
<u>in the object's shape and uncertainties in measuring contribute significantly to the error. Any error in</u>
<u>measuring a dimension is multiplied when using the volume formulas.</u>
_____
_____

Densities (from CRC Handbook):
zinc = 7.14 g/mL
copper = 8.92 g/mL
lead = 11.3 g/mL

$$\text{Percent error} = \frac{\text{Observed} - \text{Actual}}{\text{Actual}} \times 100\%$$

$$\text{Percent difference} = \frac{\text{Larger} - \text{Smaller}}{\text{Average}} \times 100\%$$

Possible grading scale:
A: 0–5% error
B: 5.1–10.0% error
C: 10.1–15.0% error
D: Over 15% error

4A Energies of Electrons

Prelab

Concepts

Gamma rays, x-rays, microwaves, radio waves, and visible light all have something in common: they are all forms of electromagnetic radiation. The term **electromagnetic radiation** expresses two main characteristics of this form of energy. *Electromagnetic* means that the energy can travel by a combination of an electrical field and a magnetic field. *Radiation* means that the energy can travel through a vacuum. Figure 4A-1 displays the various forms of electromagnetic radiation. Any display of radiant energy organized in order of wavelength is called a spectrum. (The plural is *spectra*.)

Scientists use the powerful tool of spectroscopy to study the way in which electromagnetic radiation interacts with matter. Although any form of electromagnetic radiation could theoretically be used in spectroscopy, scientists often work with visible light because it is easiest to observe. Visible light, like other kinds of electromagnetic radiation, can be either emitted or absorbed by atoms. Therefore, two kinds of visible light spectra can be distinguished: emission and absorption.

Emission spectra (or bright-line spectra) show bright lines or bands of color on a dark background. These bright lines are emitted when atoms receive energy that causes one or more of the atom's valence electrons to become "excited." The excited electrons jump from their original positions to higher-energy orbitals and almost immediately fall back to lower orbitals, thereby producing visible light. The wavelengths (colors) of the light depend on the energy differences between the atom's various orbitals. As a result, atoms of each element generate characteristic lines of colors.

Absorption spectra have intermittent dark lines on a colored background. Incandescent substances, such as lamp filaments, emit a broad, continuous range of wavelengths known as a **continuous spectrum**. Because the atoms are packed closely together in these sources, the emitted lines of color overlap and merge into a continuous spectrum.

Electromagnetic radiation that is composed of more than one wavelength (color) can be separated into its component wavelengths by a prism. Another tool that can separate component wavelengths is a diffraction grating. Although the separation of light with a diffraction grating involves different principles from separating it with a prism, the results are essentially the same—you get a spectrum.

In this experiment, you will observe the emission spectra of several salts using a simple diffraction grating spectroscope. You will sketch these spectra and then use your sketches to identify an unknown salt.

Goals

✓ Observe how a simple diffraction grating spectroscope operates.

✓ Observe and draw the spectra of several elements.

Materials

Bunsen burner

chloride salts of lithium, potassium, strontium, sodium, calcium, and copper (II)

colored pencils (*optional*)

diffraction grating spectroscope

incandescent light

matches

presoaked wooden splints

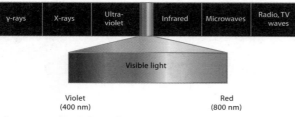

4A-1 The electromagnetic spectrum

Materials

Spectroscopes for student use are available for less than $10 from science suppliers such as Fisher Scientific, Ward's Natural Science, and Sargent-Welch.

Soak wooden splints in distilled water for at least twelve hours.

You can use other salts, but you should test them first.

In general, spectro*metry* is more quantitative than spectro*scopy*, even though the terms are often used interchangeably.

See the facet on page 77 in the student text for a full description of spectroscopy.

A diffraction grating is composed of many closely spaced grooves or lines that diffract light, resulting in a spectrum. A prism separates light by using the property of refraction.

Use labeled watch glasses for the salts.

Checkup

1. What two characteristics do all forms of energy known as electro-magnetic radiation have in common? <u>They all can travel</u> <u>through a vacuum by electric and magnetic fields.</u>

2. What region of the electromagnetic spectrum is commonly used in spectroscopy? Why? <u>Visible light is used because it is the</u> <u>easiest to observe.</u>

3. What is the difference between an emission spectrum and an absorption spectrum? <u>An emission spectrum is composed of</u> <u>bright lines on a dark background and is emitted from "excited"</u> <u>electrons. An absorption spectrum has a colored background</u> <u>with intermittent dark lines.</u>

4. What instrument will you use in this experiment? <u>a diffraction grating spectroscope</u>

5. Which of the two types of visible light spectra will you observe? <u>an emission spectrum</u>

Procedure

1. Observe a continuous spectrum by looking at an incandescent light with your spectrometer. Note the calibration marks (400–800 nm) along the bottom of the box for lithium chloride in the Data section. Add the letters ROYGBIV (representing *r*ed, *o*range, *y*ellow, *g*reen, *b*lue, *i*ndigo, and *v*iolet) at the appropriate locations in each box.

2. Light your Bunsen burner. Adjust the burner until it produces a blue or colorless flame.

3. Dip a presoaked splint into the lithium chloride. (See Figure 4A-3.)

4. Have your lab partner look through the spectrometer at the flame. Put the tip of the splint in the flame long enough for the salt to burn.

5. Have your lab partner observe the spectrum that forms. Remoisten and redip the stick if necessary. Sketch the spectrum at the appropriate calibration marks. (Record: 1.) Either label or color the bright lines to identify them. Switch roles with your lab partner so that each of you observes the burning splints using the spectrometer.

6. Repeat Steps 3–5 for the remaining known salts and an unknown salt, using a new splint for each test. (Record: 2–7.)

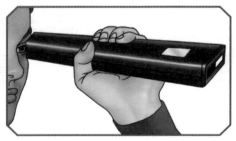

4A-2 Use of a diffraction grating spectrometer

Data

1. Lithium chloride

| | | | | | | | | | | | | | | | | | | | | |
|400| |500| |600| |700| |800|

2. Potassium chloride

| | | | | | | | | | | | | | | | | | | | | |
|400| |500| |600| |700| |800|

3. Strontium chloride

| | | | | | | | | | | | | | | | | | | | | |
|400| |500| |600| |700| |800|

4. Sodium chloride

| | | | | | | | | | | | | | | | | | | | | |
|400| |500| |600| |700| |800|

5. Calcium chloride

| | | | | | | | | | | | | | | | | | | | | |
|400| |500| |600| |700| |800|

6. Copper (II) chloride

| | | | | | | | | | | | | | | | | | | | | |
|400| |500| |600| |700| |800|

7. Unknown salt

| | | | | | | | | | | | | | | | | | | | | |
|400| |500| |600| |700| |800|

4A-3 Technique for lighting the salt

After the students have observed and drawn all six spectra, choose one of the six salts for each group and place it in an unmarked watch glass to see whether the students can identify it according to their data.

Analysis

1. Since each element produces a characteristic spectrum, what can you conclude about the location of the electrons?

   The electrons are located in definite energy levels.

2. If you had observed only the color of the flame as the salt burned, you would have conducted a flame test. Would you say that a flame test or a spectroscopic test is more accurate? Why?

   The spectrometer is more accurate for identifying elements because it breaks the color displayed in the flame

   into a characteristic spectrum of lines whose wavelengths can be quantified.

3. Suppose that you had used the same wooden splint to burn all the salts in the flame. What difficulty could this have introduced?

   Contamination of each salt with the previous one would have ruined the results and made identification

   uncertain.

4. Helium was discovered in the sun before it was discovered on the earth. How could this be?

   Scientists analyzed the light from the sun and found a spectrum that they had never seen before.

5. What was the identity of your unknown salt?

   Answers will vary, depending on which salt the teacher gave the student.

4B Mixtures of Isotopes

Prelab

Concepts

Isotopes are two or more atoms of the same element with the same number of protons (atomic number) but different numbers of neutrons. Naturally occurring elements are usually mixtures of isotopes. This is why the atomic masses listed on the periodic table are not whole numbers. Instead, they are the weighted averages of the various isotopes of each element.

You can calculate atomic mass by using the following formula:

$$\text{weighted average} = \frac{\text{total mass of atoms}}{\text{total number of atoms}}.$$

To determine the total mass, you must first determine how much mass each kind of atom (isotope) contributes. The formula for this calculation is

$$\text{total mass} = \overbrace{\text{mass of one atom}_1 \times \text{number of atoms}_1}^{\text{Isotope 1}} + \overbrace{\text{mass of one atom}_2 \times \text{number of atoms}_2}^{\text{Isotope 2}}.$$

In this experiment, you will use a mixture of two varieties of chocolate-covered candies to represent two different isotopes in 1 mol of the "element" *ememium*.

Checkup

1. What are isotopes?

    Isotopes are atoms with the same number of protons but with

    a different number of neutrons.

2. How many "isotopes" will you have in your "isotopic" mixture in this experiment?

    two

3. Why are most of the atomic masses on the periodic table not whole numbers?

    Most naturally occurring elements are isotopic mixtures, and

    their atomic masses are weighted averages.

4. An imaginary element *candium* contains two isotopes. In the naturally occurring mixture, 70.00% of the atoms are Cn-286, and 30.00% are Cn-288. Calculate the atomic mass of naturally occurring candium. Express your answer to one decimal place.

    286.6 g

Procedure

1. Obtain your mixture of candies.

2. Find the mass of five large candies and five small candies.
    (Record: 1–2.)

Goals

✓ Calculate the weighted average of an "isotopic" mixture.

✓ Calculate the percentage of each "isotope" in a mixture.

Materials

balance

50 chocolate-covered candies of two different varieties

Materials

Give each group approximately fifty M&M's in a mixture of either plain and peanut M&M's or mini and regular M&M's. You may also use another brand of a similar candy. Emphasize that the candies represent isotopes of the same element.

3. Divide each mass by 5 to get an average mass for each type of candy. (Record: 3–4.) Use SDs properly!

4. Count the number of large candies and the number of small candies. (Record: 5–6.)

Remind students to follow the rules for significant digits when adding, multiplying, and dividing.

Data

1. Mass of five large candies _____ g

2. Mass of five small candies _____ g

3. Average mass of one large candy (m_l) _____ g

4. Average mass of one small candy (m_s) _____ g

5. Number of large candies in the mixture (n_l) _____ candies

6. Number of small candies in the mixture (n_s) _____ candies

In one set of calculations, students will find the weighted average mass of one "atom" of this element—an average piece of candy in the mixture—by knowing the number of pieces and the average mass of each variety of candy in the mixture. Then they will reverse the process and find the percentages of each "isotope" (variety of candy) in the mixture, assuming you know the weighted average mass of an "atom" and the average masses of each variety of candy in the mixture. Either approach should result in the same answers (or very close). Of course, counting and weighing individual candies—the first approach—is easy, but for actual atoms of elements, this is not possible and the second approach is easier.

Analysis

1. Calculate the weighted average of the masses of candies in the mixture, as instructed below. Be sure to follow the significant digit rules. *Show your work in the margin.*

   a. Without weighing them, calculate the total mass of your sample of candies according to the following equation, where *l* represents large candies and *s* represents small candies.

   $$m_{total} = (m_l \times n_l) + (m_s \times n_s) = \text{_____} g$$

   b. Now calculate the weighted average of each candy piece as follows.

   $$\text{weighted average} = \frac{m_{total}}{\text{total number of candies } (n_l + n_s)} = \text{_____} g$$

2. Calculate the percentage of each "isotope" in the candy mixture, as explained below. (*Reminder*: Always follow significant digit rules for all mathematical operations.)

   a. Using average *masses*, solve for the percentage of each type of candy ("isotope") according to the following equation. Substitute your calculated value for the weighted average and the masses from above; then solve for x and $(1 - x)$. Let x be the fraction that is m_l, and let $(1 - x)$ be the fraction that is m_s. Once you have values for x and $(1 - x)$, express each as a percent.

   weighted average = $(x \times m_l) + [(1 - x) \times m_s]$ _____ % large candies _____ % small candies

   b. Now verify your calculations from 2a, using the formulas below, where the actual *numbers* of candies ("isotopes") are used.

   _____ % large candies _____ % small candies

   $$\% \text{ large candies} = \frac{n_l}{\text{total number}} \times 100$$

   $$\% \text{ small candies} = \frac{n_s}{\text{total number}} \times 100$$

   c. Account for any differences between the answers for 2a and 2b.

   The percentages should be close; any small differences are due to using rounded values in calculations.

5 Periodic Trends

Prelab

Concepts

The periodic law states that many properties of the elements are periodic functions of an element's atomic number. A periodic function goes through cycles with high and low values at regular intervals. Your text discusses periodic properties such as atomic radii, ionic radii, ionization energies, electron affinities, and electronegativities.

The periodic table is arranged so that all the elements that appear in similar positions in the cycle of properties are in the same vertical column in the table. For example, since Li, Na, K, Rb, and Cs appear at the maximum points in the cycle for atomic radii, they are placed in the same vertical column. Vertical columns are called *groups* or *families*, and horizontal rows are called *periods* or *series*. Properties vary according to a pattern as you move across a period or down a group.

In this laboratory exercise, you will graph the atomic radii of elements from several periods and one group from the periodic table. You will then use these graphs to predict the atomic radii of other elements. In the first graph, you will find a decrease in the atom's size as you move across a period. This decrease is caused by the increasing attraction between the opposite charges of the nucleus (+) and the valence electrons (−) as electrons and protons are added. The decrease in size continues until the noble gas of that period is reached, and then the atom's size suddenly increases. This apparent increase is more a result of the different measurement technique required for noble gas atoms than an actual increase in radius. The size increases again as you proceed from one period to the next. This time it is the result of adding an energy level. In the second graph, the addition of energy levels causes an increase in size as you proceed down a group.

Goals

✓ Demonstrate periodic patterns by graphing atomic radii and their atomic numbers.

✓ Predict other atomic radii based on these periodic patterns.

Materials

metric ruler
periodic table

Checkup

1. Define *atomic radius*. the distance from the nucleus to the
   outermost energy level of an atom

2. The sizes of atoms and ions and the forces between the nucleus and electrons are direct offshoots of electron configurations. Would you say that the electron configurations are periodic? Why?
   Yes, the periodic table is arranged by atomic number and
   electron configuration.

3. State the periodic law. Many of the properties of the elements are periodic functions of their atomic number.

4. What is a periodic function?
   a function that goes through cycles with high and low values at
   regular intervals

We cannot assume that a given atom has a definite size under all conditions any more than we can assume that the electrons in an atom are in definite orbits. Since the radius of an isolated individual atom cannot be measured, the atomic radii in the literature often vary with the source, based on the method used and the conditions under which they were measured. The data points in this table are estimates obtained by different methods. For metals, the radius is one-half the distance between the atoms' centers in metal crystals (where metal atoms are packed like stacks of spheres); for nonmetals, covalent radii in molecules of elements are used (measured as one-half the distance between atoms' centers in the bonded molecule). Since the noble gases do not form compounds and are monatomic, their radii are from van der Waals radii (similar to stacked spheres). This can account for the failure of noble gases to follow the general trend. Atomic radii in bonded molecules, where electrons are *shared* between nuclei, are expected to be smaller than those in unbonded atoms. Despite the dificulties in obtaining the data, the general trend and the periodic nature of this property should be clear.

5. What periodic property will you be graphing?

atomic radii

Procedure

1. Using the data in Table 5-1, plot the atomic radii of all 36 listed elements. (They represent elements in Periods 1–4 and the first two elements in Period 5.) Plot the atomic radii on the *y*-axis and the atomic number on the *x*-axis. Use the grid provided in the Data section. (Record: 1.) Using a ruler, connect each consecutive point with a straight line and label the major peaks on the graph with the symbol of the appropriate element.

5-1 Atomic Radii of the Elements in Nanometers

Element	Atomic number	Atomic radius (nm)	Element	Atomic number	Atomic radius (nm)
H	1	0.030	Ca	20	0.197
He	2	0.093	Sc	21	0.160
Li	3	0.152	Ti	22	0.146
Be	4	0.111	V	23	0.131
B	5	0.088	Cr	24	0.125
C	6	0.077	Mn	25	0.129
N	7	0.070	Co	27	0.126
O	8	0.066	Ni	28	0.124
F	9	0.064	Cu	29	0.128
Ne	10	0.112	Zn	30	0.133
Na	11	0.186	Ga	31	0.122
Al	13	0.143	Ge	32	0.122
Si	14	0.117	As	33	0.121
P	15	0.110	Se	34	0.117
S	16	0.104	Br	35	0.114
Cl	17	0.099	Kr	36	0.169
Ar	18	0.154	Rb	37	0.244
K	19	0.231	Sr	38	0.215

2. Using the data in Table 5-2, plot the atomic radii of the Group I elements. Plot the atomic radii on the *y*-axis and the atomic number on the *x*-axis. Use the grid provided in the Data section. (Record: 2.) Connect the data points with a smooth curve.

5-2 Atomic Radii of the Group I Elements

Element	Atomic number	Atomic radius (nm)
H	1	0.030
Li	3	0.152
K	19	0.231
Rb	37	0.244
Fr	87	0.270

Data

Horizontal Trend of Atomic Radii

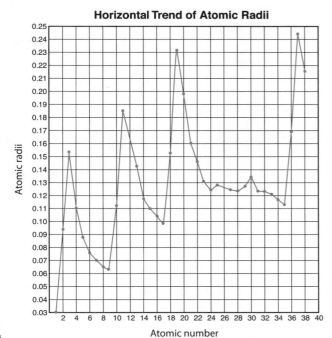

5-1   Horizontal trend of atomic radii

Vertical Trend of Atomic Radii

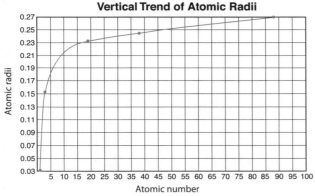

5-2   Vertical trend of atomic radii

The students should have used the elements to the left and right of Mg and Fe to make their predictions in Question 3. This method is most successful when the elements in question lie in the middle of a period and not at the end because there is a jump in the values at the end of a cycle. For example, if the students attempt to predict the radius of Na from the values before it (O, F, and Ne) and the values after it (Mg, Al, and Si), then they will make wrong predictions. In this case, it is best to look at the vertical trend; that is, the one within the group. This is what they do on Graph 5-2.

Analysis

Graph 5-1: Horizontal Trend of Atomic Radii

1. Which elements occupy the peaks in the cycles on Graph 5-1?

   Li, Na, K, and Rb

2. Do the periods, or cycles, each contain the same number of elements in Graph 5-1?

   no

3. Using Graph 5-1, predict the radii of Mg and Fe.

   Mg is 0.160 nm and Fe is 0.126 nm.

4. Compare your atomic radii values for Mg and Fe to the actual values obtained from your teacher. What is your percent error for each element? (Show your setups in the space provided.)

   $$\text{Percent error} = \frac{|\text{Observed} - \text{Actual}|}{\text{Actual}} \times 100\%$$

   _____ % (Mg)

   _____ % (Fe)

Graph 5-2: Vertical Trend of Atomic Radii

5. Look at the curve obtained in Graph 5-2. Is it in a form you would expect for elements within a group? Explain.

   Yes. There is an increase in size with atomic number in the group due to an increasing number of energy levels.

6. Using Graph 5-2, predict the atomic radii of Na and Cs.

   Na is 0.186 nm and Cs is 0.262 nm.

7. Compare your atomic radii values for Na and Cs to the actual values obtained from your teacher. What is your percent error for each element? (Show your setups in the space provided.)

   _____ % (Na)

   _____ % (Cs)

6 Bond Types

Prelab

Concepts

Ionic, covalent, and metallic bonds largely determine the physical properties of substances. Therefore, if you observe the physical properties of a substance, you can often determine its bond type. Notice in Table 6-1 the properties that result from each bond type.

6-1 Bond Types		
	Ionic bond	**Covalent bond**	**Metallic bond**
Description of electrons	transferred electrons	shared electrons	free electrons
Smallest unit	formula unit	molecule	atom
Melting point	forms solids with high melting points	forms solids with low melting points; liquids; gases	forms solids with relatively high melting points
Solubility	often soluble in water but insoluble in organic solvents	usually insoluble in water but soluble in organic solvents	insoluble in both water and organic solvents
Conductivity	conducts electricity when melted or dissolved	usually does not conduct electricity	good conductor of electricity

In this experiment, you will examine the melting points, solubilities, and conductivities of several solids in order to establish the types of bonds they contain.

Checkup

1. What can you often determine from the physical properties of substances?

   You can often determine the bond type.

Goal

✓ Investigate some of the physical properties of substances containing ionic, covalent, and metallic bonds.

Materials

acetone
balance
Bunsen burner
conductivity tester
evaporating dish
iron ring
matches
ring stand
test tube rack
test tubes, 6
unknowns, 3
weighing paper
wire gauze

Materials

Use the following substances for the three unknowns and label them by number only: 1—table salt (sodium chloride, NaCl); 2—mothball crystals (para- or p-dichlorobenzene; 3—iron filings (Fe). Quantities the size of a pea should be sufficient for each group.

You should have two labeled containers for collection of wastes—one for acetone wastes and the other for aqueous wastes.

Compounds form when two or more different elements join chemically. Since this "joining" in compounds is with either a covalent or an ionic bond and not a metallic bond, some sources classify bonds as either chemical (covalent or ionic) or metallic. Most sources, however, classify all three types of bonds as chemical bonds.

Point out that most inorganic compounds contain ionic bonds, while most organic compounds contain covalent bonds. Thus, inorganic solvents usually dissolve only inorganic (ionic) compounds, while organic solvents usually dissolve only organic (covalent) compounds. The general conclusion can be made that "like dissolves like."

2. If a substance has a high melting point and is insoluble in an organic solvent, what type(s) of bond(s) could it contain?

   either ionic bonds or metallic bonds

3. If a substance has a high melting point and is soluble in water, what type(s) of bond(s) could it contain?

   ionic bonds

4. How will a conductivity tester indicate that an electrical current is flowing?

   The light bulb will glow.

Procedure

1. Obtain small samples of the three unknowns provided by your teacher. Put each sample on a separate piece of paper.

2. Observe the substances during heating.

   a. Set up an apparatus according to Figure 6-1.

   b. Place a small amount (about the size of an uncooked grain of rice) of unknown 1 in an evaporating dish. Set the dish on the wire gauze and gently heat the contents.

   c. If the unknown does not readily melt, heat it strongly for a minute or two. Describe the ease of melting. (Record: 1.) Repeat for unknowns 2 and 3. (Record: 1.)

3. Observe the solubility.

   a. Solubility in water

   Attempt to prepare a solution of unknown 1 by placing a small amount of the substance (about the size of a grain of rice) in a test tube and adding about an inch of water. Note the relative solubility. (Record: 2.) Save this sample for Step 4. Repeat the test for relative solubility with unknown 2 and then with unknown 3. (Record: 2.) Be sure to save each mixture in separate labeled test tubes for Step 4.

   b. Solubility in acetone

   Repeat the solubility test for each unknown, using similar amounts of acetone and unknown as you did for water and unknown in Step 3a. Note the relative solubility of each. (Record: 3.) Save these mixtures.

4. Observe the conductivity.

   a. Lower the two electrodes of the conductivity tester (Figure 6-2) into the mixture that you prepared for unknown 1 in Step 3a. If the sample conducts, the circuit will be complete and the light will glow. Did the sample conduct? (Record: 4.) Repeat the conductivity test for the aqueous ("water") mixtures of unknowns 2 and 3. Rinse the electrodes between tests. (Record: 4.) Pour your mixtures into the aqueous waste container when you are finished with them.

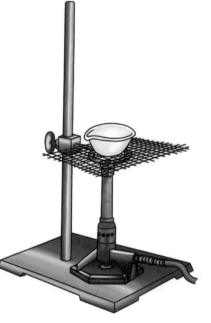

6-1   Heating apparatus

If the students do not know what "ease of melting" means, give them an example, such as "It was easy/hard to melt."

Relative solubility means all of it dissolved, some of it dissolved, or none of it dissolved.

Supplies needed to make the conductivity testers should be available at electronics stores or hobby shops. These should be prepared ahead of time.

The aqueous waste may simply be filtered, the filtrate disposed of in the sink, and the residue disposed of in the trash. The acetone wastes may be evaporated, and the residue disposed of in the trash.

b. Repeat the conductivity tests for your three unknowns, using the acetone-unknown mixtures from Step 3b. Note whether they conduct. (Record: 5.) Pour your mixtures into the acetone waste container when you are through with them.

c. Test the conductivity of the remaining small amounts of each unknown *solid* by touching the electrodes to each. (Record: 6.)

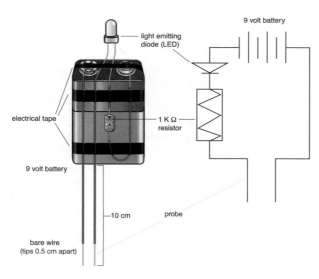

6-2 Conductivity tester and wiring diagram

Data

	Unknown 1	Unknown 2	Unknown 3
1. Melting			
2. Solubility in H$_2$O			
3. Solubility in CH$_3$COCH$_3$ (acetone)			
4. Conductivity of the aqueous mixtures			
5. Conductivity of the acetone mixtures			
6. Conductivity of the solids			

Identify the names of the unknowns at the end of the lab but before the students do the Analysis section.

Analysis

1. Identify the bond type in each of the substances tested.

    (1) salt—ionic bond; (2) naphthalene—covalent bond; (3) iron filings—metallic bond

2. On the basis of your electrical conductivity tests, describe the conductivity of the three types of bonds, both in solution and as a solid.

    In solution, ionic bonds (salt-water solution) conduct electricity, but molecular bonds (naphthalene-acetone

    solution) do not. Most metals do not dissolve in water but do conduct electricity in the solid form; the other

    solids (both ionic and molecular) do not.

3. As you will learn in more depth in Section 12A of your text, a rule of thumb that is often used in chemistry is "like dissolves like." Did the substances you used in this lab follow that rule? Explain.

    Yes, water is very polar and it dissolved the ionic compound table salt. Acetone is much less polar and it

    dissolved the nonpolar, covalent compound naphthalene.

4. Did the "solution" that you formed by mixing the metal and water conduct electricity? How do your results compare with those for the solid metal?

    No. The solid metal conducted electricity.

5. Why does an ionic solid conduct electricity only in the molten state or in an aqueous (water) solution? (*Hint*: Think about the definition of *electricity*—the movement of electrons.)

    In an aqueous solution or in the molten (liquid) state, both charged particles (ions) and electrons are free to

    move.

7 Models of Molecular Shapes

Prelab

Concepts

A covalent bond, according to the *valence bond theory*, forms when atoms share electrons in overlapping orbitals. Several things should be noted about these overlapping orbitals. First, one overlapping set of orbitals forms a single bond, two sets form a double bond, and three sets form a triple bond. Second, the bonds between atoms in a molecule are covalent bonds.

The orbitals in a molecule, whether they are bonded or unbonded, arrange themselves as far apart as possible. This arrangement results in the molecular shapes indicated in Table 7-1. You can determine the shape of a molecule from a Lewis structure. First, count the number of regions of electrons surrounding the *central* atom in the molecule. Then count the number of regions that are covalently bonded (the number of bonded nuclei).

Goals

✓ Write Lewis structures of certain molecules.

✓ Assemble three-dimensional models of these molecules.

✓ Visualize molecular polarity from the three-dimensional models.

Materials

clay

toothpicks

Materials

It is probably best, if possible, to purchase inexpensive molecular model kits from a science supplier. These will have the correct three-dimensional shapes and angles. They may also be used in Lab 18A.

To help tie everything together about covalent bonding, you may want to briefly cover the following information. It is also covered in the text. If the overlapping orbitals are both *s* orbitals, then a sigma bond results. If they are both *p* orbitals that are end to end (or "head-on"), then they also result in sigma bonds. If they are both *p* orbitals that are side by side, then a pi bond results. But if the original orbitals are of different types (for example, *s* and *p*), yet they form equivalent-energy bonds, then they are said to mix, or "hybridize," to form hybrid orbitals of equal energies. (See text art, p. 162, Figures 7-1 through 7-4.)

7-1 Molecular Shapes

Number of electron regions	Number of bonded nuclei	Geometry
4	4	tetrahedral
	3	pyramidal
	2	bent (109.5°)
	1	linear
3	3	trigonal planar
	2	bent (120°)
	1	linear
2	2	linear
	1	linear

The molecular shapes in Table 7-1 will be polar if they contain asymmetrically arranged polar bonds. Polar bonds result when different atoms in a molecule share electrons (for example, oxygen and nitrogen). Because different atoms have different electronegativities, they will not share the electrons equally; the electrons will be shifted toward the more electronegative atom. This shifting of electrons results in a semi-ionic condition that gives the covalent bond a partially negative charge and a partially positive charge—it is polar. For most purposes, carbon and hydrogen are assumed to be nearly equal in electronegativity and therefore form nonpolar covalent bonds.

Visualizing molecules as three-dimensional is essential to understanding the relationship between regions of electrons, bonded nuclei, molecular shape, and polarity. Although Lewis structures show the arrangements of atoms in a molecule, they do not give a spatial, three-dimensional view. By preparing three-dimensional models of some of the common molecules and studying Table 7-1, you should gain a good understanding of these relationships.

Checkup

1. What are the three types of bonds with which your text deals?

   metallic, ionic, and covalent

2. What type(s) of bond(s) does this laboratory exercise emphasize?

   covalent polar and nonpolar, or simply, covalent bonds

3. Define *covalent bonding*.

   According to the valence bond theory, it is the sharing of

   electrons in overlapping orbitals.

4. What two things do you have to consider when determining molecular shape?

   the number of electron regions and the number of bonded

   nuclei

5. Define what is meant by *polar bond*. If a molecule has polar bonds, is it always a polar molecule? Why or why not?

   In a polar bond, the electrons are not shared equally. The result

   is a semi-ionic condition with partially positive and partially

   negative charges. A molecule containing polar bonds is not

   polar if the bonds are symmetrically arranged.

Procedure

Complete Table 7-2. This will be your data table.

Analysis

1. If you added a hydrogen ion (H^+) to the ammonia model you made, what substance would you have? Does this additional hydrogen ion cause the shape of the new molecule to be different from ammonia? Explain.

   This would form the ammonium ion (NH_4^+). Yes, the shape would change since the shape of ammonia is

   pyramidal, and the ammonium ion is tetrahedral.

2. What is the difference between the carbon-oxygen bond in your model of methanol and the one in carbon dioxide?

   In methanol the carbon-oxygen bond is a single bond, but in carbon dioxide it is a double bond.

3. Would a dichloromethane molecule still be polar if the hydrogen and chlorine atoms were placed at the corners of a rectangle surrounding the carbon instead of in their actual locations?

   Yes, if they were at adjacent corners, the molecule would still be polar; however, if they were at opposite

   corners, it would not be polar.

4. Compare the molecular polarity of CCl_4 with CH_2Cl_2. Explain any differences.

   They are both tetrahedral, but CCl_4 is not a polar molecule because it is symmetrical. CH_2Cl_2 is polar because

   it is asymmetrical.

The IUPAC nomenclature will not be discussed until Chapter 8, but the students need to be exposed to it. Perhaps you could return to this section for a review when they have learned the IUPAC nomenclature.

7-2   Molecular Shape Data

IUPAC name formula common name	methanal CH₂O formaldehyde	methane CH₄	dihydrogen oxide H₂O water	nitrogen trihydride NH₃ ammonia	carbon dioxide CO₂	methanol CH₃OH	hydrogen cyanide HCN	dichloromethane CH₂Cl₂ methylene chloride	tetrachloromethane CCl₄ carbon tetrachloride
1. What is the electron-dot structure?	H : C :: O :	H : C : H (with H above and below)	: O : H (with H below)	: N : H (with H above and below)	: O :: C :: O :	H : C : O : H (with H above and below)	H : C ::: N :	H : C : Cl : (with H above, Cl below)	: Cl : C : Cl : (with Cl above and below)
2. How many regions of electrons surround the central atom?	3	4	4	4	2	4	2	4	4
3. How many atoms surround the central atom?	3	4	2	3	2	4	2	4	4
4. Make a model of this shape and sketch it.									
5. What is the molecular shape from Table 7-1?	trigonal planar	tetrahedral	bent	pyramidal	linear	tetrahedral	linear	tetrahedral	tetrahedral
6. Does the molecule contain polar bonds?	yes	no	yes	yes	yes	yes	yes	yes	yes
7. Is the entire molecule polar?	yes	no	yes	yes	no	yes	yes	yes	no

5. Which of the compounds in this exercise are organic according to the definition in Section 18A of your textbook?

methanal, methane, methanol, hydrogen cyanide, dichloromethane, and tetrachloromethane

8 Reactions and Equations

Prelab

Concepts

In this experiment, you will perform a series of reactions involving copper and some of its compounds. For each chemical reaction involved, you will write a chemical equation. A chemical equation represents changes that occur during chemical reactions. In order for a chemical equation to be correct, it must be balanced; that is, there must be the same number of each kind of atom on both sides of the arrow.

Although there are many types of chemical reactions, you will be asked to classify each reaction according to one of three general types: synthesis, decomposition, and replacement. **Synthesis reactions** combine two or more substances into a single product. In contrast, **decomposition reactions** break down a single substance into two or more products. The third type, called **replacement reactions**, involves compounds that swap elements, and often produce a precipitate. In a **single replacement reaction**, an active element takes the place of a less active element in a compound. In a **double replacement reaction**, two compounds swap elements with each other.

Of the three types of chemical reactions, replacement reactions are the most difficult to accurately represent by a chemical equation. This is true because most replacement reactions take place in water where the reactants exist as ions, not as molecules. It is customary to write ionic equations in net ionic form. In this method, only those ions taking part in the reaction are written. Other ions present in the solution but not involved in the reaction are known as **spectator ions**, and they are not included in the equation. For example, the net ionic equation for the reaction of KCl and $AgNO_3$ solution would be this:

$$Ag^+ + Cl^- \longrightarrow AgCl\ (s).$$

This net ionic equation came from canceling out any spectator ions in the following molecular form of the equation:

$$KCl + AgNO_3 \longrightarrow KNO_3 + AgCl.$$

Even though it is not customary, you will write the equations for the copper reactions in this experiment in the molecular form. You do not need to proceed to the ionic form because it involves several concepts you will not learn until later in the text.

Checkup

1. What is the word equation for the reaction that forms water from oxygen and hydrogen? <u>oxygen + hydrogen ⟶ water</u>

2. The reaction between aqueous solutions of hydrochloric acid and sodium hydroxide produces table salt (sodium chloride) and water. Is the following chemical equation in the customary form for this reaction? Why or why not?

$$HCl + NaOH \longrightarrow NaCl + HOH$$

<u>No, it is not in the customary form. It is in a water solution, and</u>

<u>the customary form of this equation is the net ionic form.</u>

Goals

✓ Observe the changes that take place during chemical reactions.

✓ Write chemical equations to describe chemical reactions.

Materials

beakers, 150 mL and 250 mL
Bunsen burner
clay triangle
copper wool
crucible
crucible tongs
filtering funnel
filter paper
glass stirring rod
graduated cylinders, 10 mL and 25 mL
iron ring
matches
ring stand
sodium hydroxide (NaOH), 3 *M*
sulfuric acid (H_2SO_4), 6 *M*
waste container

Materials

Students MUST wear gloves, goggles, and aprons for this lab.

As a precaution, you should have the following available in the lab: a saturated boric acid solution for contact with bases and a saturated sodium bicarbonate solution for contact with acids. Pouring the appropriate solution on the affected area, followed by plenty of rinsing, should be sufficient for most accidental acid and base contact.

Have a labeled container for collection of chemical waste in Step 5 of the Procedure section.

Each group will need about 1 g of copper wool.

Acid-base and redox reactions are examples of other types of reactions.

When ions combine, an insoluble product is usually formed, which leaves the solution as a precipitate, gas, or new molecular substance.

3. What type of chemical reaction often produces a precipitate?

   a replacement reaction

4. What two types of chemical reactions are opposites of each other?

   synthesis and decomposition reactions

5. How do you know when you have a balanced equation?

   The number of each type of atom is the same on both sides of

   the equation.

Procedure

1. *Synthesis Reaction*

   a. Make a loose wad of copper wool and place it in a crucible.

   b. Set up an apparatus as shown in Lab 9A, Figure 9A-1. Place the crucible, uncovered, on a clay triangle and heat it strongly for about 5 minutes. A black product results from the reaction of copper with atmospheric oxygen. What is this black product? (Record: 1.)

2. *Double Replacement Reaction*

   a. Using crucible tongs, dump the black product from the crucible into a 150 mL beaker.

   b. Obtain 5 mL of 6 *M* H_2SO_4 in a graduated cylinder.

   c. Add the sulfuric acid to the black product in the beaker, and carefully stir the mixture with a glass stirring rod. Some of the black product will dissolve in the sulfuric acid. What two products result from this double replacement reaction? (Record: 2.) What is the color of this solution? (Record: 3.)

   d. Prepare a filtering funnel and set it in the clay triangle on the iron ring.

   e. Filter the solution into a 250 mL beaker and save the filtrate in the beaker for the next step. The filter paper can be thrown out.

3. *Double Replacement Reaction*

   a. Obtain approximately 20 mL of 6 *M* NaOH in a clean 25 mL graduated cylinder.

   b. Add 10 mL of the sodium hydroxide from the graduated cylinder to the filtrate in the beaker as you stir the mixture. A precipitate will form.

   c. Add additional sodium hydroxide while you stir the mixture until no more precipitate forms. What are the two products of this double replacement reaction? (Record: 4.)

4. *Decomposition Reaction*

   a. *Cautiously* boil the mixture from Step 3c until a reaction takes place. (Alkaline solutions tend to spatter!) Water and copper (II) oxide will form.

   b. What is the reactant that decomposed? (Record: 5.)

5. Pour your mixture from Step 4 into the waste container provided.

Filter the collected waste to remove the CuO, which may be discarded in the trash. Neutralize the filtrate with 6 *M* hydrochloric acid and flush it down the drain.

Data

1. What is the black product that resulted from the reaction of copper and atmospheric oxygen?

   copper (II) oxide, CuO

2. What two products resulted from the addition of sulfuric acid to the black compound?

   water and copper (II) sulfate, $CuSO_4$

3. What was the color of the solution after the sulfuric acid was added to the black compound?

   blue

4. What were the two products that resulted from the double replacement reaction of sodium hydroxide and the filtrate?

   copper (II) hydroxide, $Cu(OH)_2$, and sodium sulfate, Na_2SO_4

5. When you heated the filtrate, what compound decomposed into copper (II) oxide (CuO) and water?

   copper (II) hydroxide, $Cu(OH)_2$

Analysis

1. Write a word equation and a balanced equation for the synthesis reaction in which copper and atmospheric oxygen produced the black compound.

   copper + oxygen $\longrightarrow$ copper (II) oxide

   $2Cu + O_2 \longrightarrow 2CuO$

2. Write a word equation and a balanced equation for the double replacement reaction resulting from the addition of sulfuric acid to the black compound.

   copper (II) oxide + sulfuric acid $\longrightarrow$ copper (II) sulfate + water

   $CuO + H_2SO_4 \longrightarrow CuSO_4 + H_2O$

3. What ion do you think caused the color change of the solution of sulfuric acid and the black compound? What evidence do you have for your answer?

   The Cu^{2+} ion. The ions of the sulfuric acid were already in solution, and none of them had any color.

   When the copper (II) oxide (the black compound) was added to the solution of sulfuric acid, the Cu^{2+} ions

   were released and caused the blue color.

4. Write a word equation and a balanced equation for the double replacement reaction resulting from the addition of sodium hydroxide to the colored filtrate.

   copper (II) sulfate + sodium hydroxide $\longrightarrow$ sodium sulfate + copper (II) hydroxide

   $CuSO_4 + 2NaOH \longrightarrow Na_2SO_4 + Cu(OH)_2$

Look for good, thoughtful explanations on this question rather than just a correct answer.

5. Write a word equation and a balanced equation for the decomposition reaction resulting in the products copper (II) oxide and water.

copper (II) hydroxide $\xrightarrow{\text{heat}}$ copper (II) oxide + water

$Cu(OH)_2 \xrightarrow{\Delta} CuO + H_2O$

9A Empirical Formulas

Prelab

Concepts

The law of definite composition states that every compound has a definite composition by mass (percent composition). This means that substances combine in definite ratios to form compounds. These ratios can be expressed by formulas. The formula that expresses the simplest whole-number ratio for a compound is called an **empirical formula**. For example, for every potassium atom in the formula $KClO_3$, there is one chlorine atom and three oxygen atoms—a ratio of 1:1:3. Since this formula expresses the simplest whole-number ratio for potassium chlorate, it is the empirical formula.

You can determine empirical formulas experimentally by establishing the mass of each element present in a compound. To do this, you must carry out at least one chemical reaction involving that substance and another. For example, in this experiment you will synthesize magnesium oxide from its elements, magnesium and oxygen. You will also determine the mass of the magnesium before the synthesis and the mass of the magnesium oxide after the synthesis. Subtracting the mass of the magnesium from the mass of the magnesium oxide gives you the mass of the oxygen used in the synthesis reaction. From these masses you can find the number of moles of each element. Since the mole ratio must equal the ratio of atoms in the compound, you can easily find the empirical formula.

Checkup

1. What is the ratio of particles in the compound calcium sulfate?

   Since the formula is $CaSO_4$, the ratio is 1:1:4.

2. What is the percent by mass of sodium in NaOH?

   (Divide the mass of the *part* by the mass of the *whole*; then multiply by 100%.)

   $$\frac{22.99 \text{ g Na}}{39.998 \text{ g NaOH}} \times 100\% = 57.48\% \text{ Na by mass}$$

3. Define *empirical formula*.

   the formula of a compound that expresses the simplest whole-number ratio of its components

4. What is the empirical formula of $C_6H_{12}O_6$?

   CH_2O

5. Air is a mixture of mostly nitrogen and oxygen gases. When magnesium burns in air, most of the magnesium combines with oxygen to form magnesium oxide, MgO; however, some of the magnesium combines with nitrogen to form magnesium nitride, Mg_3N_2. To avoid this problem, you will add water in Step 3 of the procedure. Adding water to magnesium nitride and heating the mixture converts it to magnesium oxide and produces ammonia gas, NH_3. Write

Goals

✓ Observe the law of definite composition.

✓ Calculate percent composition.

✓ Derive an empirical formula.

✓ Develop chemical equations.

Materials

balance
Bunsen burner
clay triangle
crucible and cover
crucible tongs
iron ring
magnesium ribbon
matches
paper towel
ring stand
sandpaper
transfer pipet (eyedropper)

the balanced equation for the reaction between magnesium nitride and water.

$$Mg_3N_2 + 3H_2O \xrightarrow{\Delta} 3MgO + 2NH_3$$

Procedure

1. Prepare the materials.

   a. Clean your crucible and cover with soap and water; rinse them well. Support them on a ring with a clay triangle. The crucible cover should be tilted on the top of the crucible, leaving a small opening. (See Figure 9A-1.)

9A-1 Crucible and cover

   b. Heat the crucible and cover for three minutes to drive off any moisture.

   c. When it is cool, find the mass of the crucible with its cover. (Record: 1.)

   d. Clean a strip of magnesium ribbon approximately 30 cm long with sandpaper to remove the oxide coating; then wipe it off with a dry paper towel.

   e. Roll up the magnesium and place it in the crucible in such a way that a good portion of the ribbon is in contact with the bottom and lower sides of the crucible. Portions of the ribbon that are too far away from the heat source may not react completely, thereby giving poor results.

   f. Replace the cover and find the mass of the crucible, the cover, and the magnesium. (Record: 2.)

If the students apply the small inner cone of a well-adjusted flame to the bottom of the crucible, then the crucible bottom will glow bright red within three minutes. Avoid a yellow flame because it deposits soot on the bottom of the crucible, and this will affect the mass.

2. Burn the magnesium strip in air to produce magnesium oxide.

   a. Place the crucible and its contents on the clay triangle and start heating them. You should remove the cover but hold it nearby with your tongs. The moment the magnesium starts to burn, place the cover on the crucible.

   b. Continue taking the cover on and off every 1–2 minutes using crucible tongs until the magnesium fails to glow when the cover is removed. At this point, heat the covered crucible as hot as possible for several additional minutes.

3. Add water; then heat to convert the magnesium nitride.

   a. Allow the covered crucible to cool for about ten minutes. It will cool faster if allowed to do so on a wire gauze placed on your desktop. Uniformly distribute ten drops of distilled water from your transfer pipet over the crucible contents, replace the cover, and heat carefully until the water evaporates; then heat strongly for several minutes. Do you detect any recognizable odor? If so, what does it smell like? (Record: 5.)

   b. Cool the crucible for about five minutes. Repeat the instructions in Step 3a once.

   c. Allow the crucible, the cover, and the contents to cool to room temperature, and then find the mass. (Record: 3.)

   d. To make sure that the water is gone, reheat the covered crucible for several minutes, cool it to room temperature, and find the mass again. (Record: 4.) This mass should be very close (within a few hundredths of a gram) to the one recorded from Step 3c. If it is not, repeat this step until you obtain two masses that agree.

Data

1. Mass of crucible and cover   ———— g

2. Mass of crucible, cover, and magnesium   ———— g

3. Mass of crucible, cover, and magnesium oxide—
first mass   ———— g

4. Mass of crucible, cover, and magnesium oxide—
second mass   ———— g

5. What was the odor you detected? <u>ammonia</u>

Analysis

1. What was the mass of the magnesium?   ———— g

2. What was the mass of the compound magnesium oxide?   ———— g

3. What was the mass of the oxygen that chemically combined with the magnesium?   ———— g

Remind the students to use distilled water for this procedure if your tap water is very hard.

4. What is the empirical formula for the magnesium oxide?

   a. Use the atomic masses of oxygen and magnesium to calculate the moles of each element.   _____ mol O

                                                        _____ mol Mg

   b. Divide both moles by the smaller number of moles to get the mole ratio. If necessary, multiply by a whole number to get the ratio in whole numbers.   <u> 1:1 </u>

   c. Determine the empirical formula.   <u> MgO   </u>

5. Find your percent error.

   a. Using the masses of magnesium and magnesium oxide obtained experimentally, calculate the *observed* (experimental) percentage of magnesium in your magnesium oxide.   _____ % Mg

   b. Calculate the *actual* % Mg from the formula, MgO (see text, Subsection 9.12).   _____ % Mg

   c. Calculate your percent error using the formula for percent error given below.   _____ %

$$\text{Percent error} = \frac{|\text{Observed} - \text{Actual}|}{\text{Actual}} \times 100\%$$

6. Write the balanced equation for the reaction of magnesium with oxygen gas to form magnesium oxide. Since atmospheric oxygen is a diatomic element, use O_2 in the reaction.

<u>$2Mg + O_2 \longrightarrow 2MgO$ </u>

9B Formulas of Hydrates

Prelab

Concepts

A **hydrate** is a compound that has water molecules in its crystalline structure. Most hydrates are a combination of a salt crystal and water. When the salt and water unite, they do so in a specific ratio. For example, calcium sulfate dihydrate, also known as gypsum, contains 1 mole of the salt $CaSO_4$ for every 2 moles of water. This produces the hydrate $CaSO_4 \cdot 2H_2O$.

The water that is incorporated into the crystal structure of a hydrate is called the **water of hydration**. Waters of hydration can be driven out of a hydrate by low pressures or high temperatures. But some hydrates lose some or all of their waters of hydration naturally. These hydrates are called **efflorescent**. There are also substances that attract water when placed in the open air at room temperature. These substances are called **hygroscopic** compounds.

In this experiment, you will use heat to drive off the waters of hydration. When a hydrate is heated, the products are water (which is driven off) and an anhydrous salt (**anhydrous** means "without water"). By determining the moles of anhydrous salt left and the moles of water driven off, you can determine the formula of the hydrate.

Checkup

1. What is the formula of magnesium carbonate trihydrate?

   $MgCO_3 \cdot 3H_2O$

2. What is the name for the hydrate $CoCl_2 \cdot 2H_2O$?

   cobalt (II) chloride dihydrate

3. What are the two ways that waters of hydration can be driven off? Which method will you be using?

   lowered pressure and heating; heating

4. Define *hydrate*.

   Hydrates are substances that unite chemically with water to

   form dry, crystalline compounds.

5. What is the main purpose of this experiment?

   to determine the formula of a hydrate

Procedure

1. Prepare the materials.

   a. Obtain 2.0–3.0 g of a hydrate. Get its anhydrous formula from your teacher. (Record: 1.)

   b. Remove any moisture from a clean crucible and its cover by heating them with your burner for several minutes. Let them cool to room temperature, and then determine their total mass.

Goals

✓ Describe the chemical and physical properties of hydrated compounds.

✓ Determine the formula of a hydrated compound.

Materials

balance
Bunsen burner
clay triangle
crucible and cover
crucible tongs
hydrate
iron ring
matches
ring stand

Materials

The equipment setup for this procedure should be the same as for Lab 9A.

Hydrates were introduced in Subsection 8.11.

Plaster of Paris is calcium sulfate hemihydrate, $CaSO_4 \cdot \frac{1}{2}H_2O$, and is formed from the dihydrate of calcium sulfate.

If a compound is very hygroscopic and very soluble in water, then it dissolves in the water that it captures from the air. A compound like this is said to be **deliquescent**.

You can use hydrates such as copper (II) sulfate pentahydrate ($CuSO_4 \cdot 5H_2O$) or barium chloride dihydrate crystals ($BaCl_2 \cdot 2H_2O$).

Label the container with the anhydrous formula, or announce the formula to the students.

(Record: 2.) Use your crucible tongs—not your fingers—from here on when you pick up your crucible and lid.

   c. Add your sample to the crucible. Replace the cover and determine the mass of the sample and crucible. (Record: 3.)

2. Produce an anhydrous salt by heating.

   a. Place the crucible with its cover on a clay triangle.

   b. First heat the crucible over a low flame; then gradually raise the temperature. Continue to heat it for 15 minutes.

   c. Allow the crucible and cover to cool to room temperature.

   d. Determine the mass of the crucible, the cover, and the contents. (Record: 4.)

3. Show all of your calculation setups in the margin in the Analysis section and use significant digits properly.

Data

1. Formula of anhydrous salt _____

2. Mass of crucible and cover _____ g

3. Mass of crucible, cover, and hydrate _____ g

4. Mass of crucible, cover, and anhydrous salt _____ g

Analysis

1. What is the mass of the hydrate sample? _____ g

2. What is the mass of the anhydrous salt? _____ g

3. What is the mass of the water driven off by heating? _____ g

4. How many moles of anhydrous salt were in your sample? _____ moles salt

5. How many moles of water were in your sample? _____ moles water

6. What is the ratio of moles of water that would combine with 1 mole of the anhydrous salt? (Express to the proper number of decimal places.) _____ moles water/mole salt

7. Round the value obtained in Question 6 to the nearest whole number. _____

8. Give the formula of your hydrate. _____

9. What is the name of your hydrate? _____

10. Using your experimental value (6) and the exact value for the number of waters of hydration supplied by your teacher, calculate your percent error. _____ %

11. Would insufficient heating of the hydrate make your experimental value (6) too large or too small? Explain your reasoning.

   It would be too small; the moles of water calculated (the numerator) would be too small, and the moles of salt (the denominator) would be too large.

Remind students to follow the rules for significant digits. The calculations involve both multiplication/division and subtraction. They should show all of their setups for their calculations.

9C Stoichiometric Relationships

Prelab

Concepts

Carbon dioxide is a harmless gas that can be liberated easily from several carbon compounds, particularly from carbonates and bicarbonates. Because of these qualities, it is used to make bakery goods rise. During baking, carbon dioxide (CO_2) gas is released from two major sources: baking powder and baking soda ($NaHCO_3$) with an acid. Although yeast also produces CO_2, it does so by converting sugar in the dough to water and carbon dioxide, rather than actually being the source of the CO_2.

You will use baking soda in this experiment for the purpose of determining the mole ratio between a reactant and a product. Consider the following reaction of $NaHCO_3$ and the acid HCl.

$$NaHCO_3 \ (s) + HCl \ (aq) \longrightarrow NaCl \ (aq) + CO_2 \ (g) + H_2O \ (l)$$

This reaction is ideal for determining a mole ratio for several reasons. First, the reactant, $NaHCO_3$, is a dry compound, so you can measure its mass before you add HCl. Second, the reaction produces only one measurable product, NaCl. Since the CO_2 gas escapes and the water can be boiled off, you can measure the mass of just the NaCl, rather than a mixture of products.

After you complete the experiment, you will convert the measured masses of $NaHCO_3$ and NaCl to moles. Then you will compare the moles of reactant to the moles of product and establish the mole ratio. If you are careful when you determine the masses, your experimental mole ratio will equal the theoretical mole ratio given by the coefficients in the balanced equation above.

Checkup

1. What is the basic goal of this exercise?

   to determine the mole ratio between the reactant $NaHCO_3$ and

   the product NaCl

2. What experimental procedure, if carefully done, will cause this experiment to yield accurate results?

   determining the masses of the reactant $NaHCO_3$ and the

   product NaCl

3. Why is it easier to have a reaction in which only one product will remain? because you can determine the number of moles

   of that one product and compare it to the number of moles in

   one reactant

4. Why do you heat the products, determine the mass, reheat, and then determine the mass again? to make sure that all of the

   water has boiled off

Goal

✓ Demonstrate the relationship between the moles of reactant and the moles of product in a chemical reaction.

Materials

balance
beaker, 150 mL
Bunsen burner
crucible tongs
evaporating dish
hydrochloric acid (HCl), 6 M
iron ring
matches
ring stand
sodium hydrogen carbonate ($NaHCO_3$)
spatula
test tube
transfer pipet (eyedropper)
wash bottle
watch glass, small
weighing paper
wire gauze

Materials

$NaHCO_3$ is also called sodium bicarbonate.

A common test for the presence of CO_2 gas uses limewater. When CO_2 is bubbled through limewater, it causes the limewater to turn cloudy.

Commercial baking powders are made of dry baking soda mixed with an acid-forming salt that releases carbon dioxide when water is added.

5. What could cause error in your measuring the mass of NaCl?

Some NaCl could be lost by splattering, or some water may not be boiled off.

Procedure

1. Prepare the materials.

    a. Clean an evaporating dish and rinse it with distilled water from a wash bottle.

    b. Using the crucible tongs, hold the evaporating dish in a well-adjusted burner flame for several minutes to remove all the moisture.

    c. While the dish is cooling on the wire gauze, use a spatula to obtain some sodium hydrogen carbonate ($NaHCO_3$) on a piece of weighing paper.

    d. After the dish is cool, measure its mass. (Record: 1.)

    e. Using the spatula, add about 3 g of the $NaHCO_3$ to the evaporating dish while it is still on the balance. Record the combined mass of the dish and $NaHCO_3$. (Record: 2.)

2. React the $NaHCO_3$ with the HCl.

    a. Cover the evaporating dish with a small watch glass to keep materials from splattering out during the reaction.

    b. Obtain about 6 mL of 6 M HCl in a clean test tube. Gradually add the acid to the $NaHCO_3$ with a transfer pipet or dropper. Allow the drops to enter the lip of the evaporating dish so that they flow down the side gradually. (See Figure 9C-1.)

9C-1 Adding the acid slowly with an eyedropper

    c. Continue adding the acid until the reaction stops (no more fizzing). Do not add more acid than is necessary. Tilt the dish from

To properly dispose of the unused excess HCl, collect it in a container, cautiously add baking soda until the fizzing ceases, and flush the neutralized mixture down the drain with plenty of running water.

side to side to make sure that the acid has reached all of the solid.

d. Remove the watch glass and, using a transfer pipet, rinse any spattered material from the underside of the watch glass with a small amount of distilled water. Be careful to wash all of the material into the evaporating dish so that no NaCl is lost. (See Figure 9C-2.)

3. Boil off the water and determine the mass of the NaCl.

a. Place your evaporating dish on a wire gauze that is supported by an iron ring stand. Heat the water in the evaporating dish until it boils gently. Do not let the water boil over or you will lose some of the NaCl.

b. Continue to heat the dish until most of the water has evaporated. Use an air bath as you did in Lab 2A (Figure 9C-3) to dry the NaCl completely.

c. Remove the dish from the air bath and allow it to cool; then weigh it and record its mass. (Record: 3.)

d. To make sure that all of the water has been driven off, reheat the dish and contents directly on the wire gauze. Let them cool and weigh them again. (Record: 4.) If this mass does not closely agree with the mass in Step 3c, reheat, cool, and continue measuring the mass until you achieve a consistent measurement.

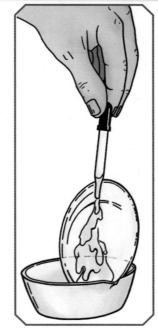

9C-2 Rinsing the watch glass with water

9C-3 Air bath

Data

1. Mass of evaporating dish _____ g

2. Mass of evaporating dish plus $NaHCO_3$ _____ g

3. Mass of evaporating dish plus NaCl—weighing 1 _____ g

4. Mass of evaporating dish plus NaCl—weighing 2 _____ g

Remind the students to use significant digits correctly.

Analysis

1. Write the balanced equation for the reaction in this experiment.

    $NaHCO_3 + HCl \longrightarrow NaCl + CO_2 + H_2O$

2. How many grams of $NaHCO_3$ reacted? _____ g

3. How many grams of NaCl were produced? _____ g

4. Calculate the number of moles of $NaHCO_3$ that were used in the reaction. (Show your setups!) _____ mol

5. Calculate the number of moles of NaCl that were produced in the reaction. (Show your setups!) _____ mol

6. Divide both of the mole amounts (4 and 5) by the smaller of the two to give your experimental ratio between $NaHCO_3$ and NaCl (x:1 or 1:x).

    $x =$ _____

7. What is the mole ratio between $NaHCO_3$ and NaCl from the balanced equation? __1:1__

8. What is your percent error? [Percent error = $(x - 1) \times 100\%$] _____ %

10A Charles's Law

Prelab

Concepts

As you learned in Chapter 10, gas molecules are normally very far apart. Consequently, both temperature and pressure have a much greater influence on the volumes of gases than on the volumes of solids or liquids. If the amount of gas and the pressure remain constant, Charles's law describes the direct relationship between the volume of a gas and its absolute (Kelvin) temperature. If we plot a graph to depict these relationships, a straight line with a positive slope results. (See Figure 10A-1.) You can see that if the temperature increases, the volume also increases proportionally; if the temperature decreases, the volume likewise decreases proportionally.

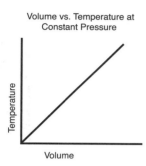

Volume vs. Temperature at Constant Pressure

10A-1   Volume vs. temperature

In this lab, you will trap a volume of air in a capillary tube and relate the length of the column to its temperature. Although the usual form of Charles's law contains volume as one of the variables, you will not actually need to calculate the volume of the trapped air because we will assume that the diameter of the capillary tube is constant over the entire length of the tube. Thus, in the formula for the volume of a cylinder ($V = \pi r^2 h$), πr^2 is constant; the volume of trapped air will be proportional to the length of the column. Using Charles's law, you will compare the calculated (theoretical) and measured lengths of the column—analogous to V_2—to find how closely they agree. You will also plot your data on graph paper and extrapolate to determine an experimental value for absolute zero—the temperature at which the volume of an ideal gas theoretically becomes zero.

Goals

✓ Experimentally determine V_2.

✓ Calculate the theoretical value for V_2, using Charles's law.

✓ Determine the percent error between the experimental and theoretical values of V_2.

✓ Experimentally determine absolute zero.

✓ Calculate the percent error between the experimental and theoretical values for absolute zero.

Materials

beaker, 600 mL
Bunsen burner
crucible tongs
glass stirring rod
ice cubes
iron ring
matches
melting point capillary tubes
metric ruler
ring stand
rubber bands, small, orthodontic
test tube clamp
thermometer
vegetable oil
watch glass
wire gauze

Materials

The melting point capillary tubes are sometimes sold as glass capillary tubes. If yours are open on both ends, you will need to heat one end enough to fuse the glass shut for this experiment. Some melting point capillary tubes are already sealed for you.

Checkup

1. If the volume of a gas changed from 255 mL to 282 mL while the amount of gas and the pressure on it remained constant, what must have happened to the temperature of the gas?

   It must have increased.

2. What type of relationship is there between volume and absolute temperature?

   a direct relationship

3. What two volumes (lengths) will you compare to obtain the percent error in verifying Charles's law in this experiment?

   the theoretical and the experimental values

4. Why must the entire length of the air column be submerged in the water bath?

   so that the entire volume of air is at the same temperature—

   that of the water bath

5. Why do you not need to calculate V_2 in this experiment in order to test Charles's law?

   The volume of trapped air is proportional to the height of the

   air column because the diameter of the tube is assumed to be

   constant over the entire length of the tube.

Procedure

1. Prepare your capillary tubes.

   a. Obtain about 10 drops of vegetable oil on your watch glass. Carefully hold one of the melting point tubes in your tongs with the open end slanted upward, and pass it through your burner flame several times. Immediately dip the open end of this heated tube into the oil on your watch glass, and allow it to cool and draw up a "plug" of oil about 1 cm long. When cooled to room temperature, the length of the trapped air should be about 5–7 cm. (If you allow the tube to get too hot, the length of trapped air will be too small, resulting in larger relative errors. If you do not heat the capillary tube enough, the air column will be too long, making it impossible for you to obtain data at higher temperatures.) Repeat the procedure with the second capillary tube.

   b. Attach the capillary tubes containing trapped air—with open ends upward—to your thermometer using two small rubber bands, as shown in Figure 10A-2.

2. Collect the data.

   a. Attach an iron ring to your ring stand at a height that will allow you to place a burner underneath it. Fill a 1000 mL beaker about two-thirds full of ice and water and place it on a wire gauze on the ring. Clamp the thermometer assembly to the ring stand and lower it into the ice-water mixture so that it is near the beaker

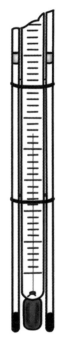

10A-2 Thermometer assembly

wall (for easier reading of the air column length). *Be sure there is enough water in the beaker so that the entire length of the air column is submerged.* (See Figure 10A-3.)

10A-3   Charles's law setup

b. Allow the tubes to remain in the ice-water bath until the temperature reaches a steady reading. Stirring the bath periodically with a stirring rod will hasten this. Once you have noted no further change in the temperature, wait several minutes before you measure the lengths of air columns in the tubes. In this cold bath, you will probably need to wipe off the condensation from the beaker to get a clear view of the capillary tubes. Carefully measure the length of the trapped air column in each tube to the nearest 0.1 cm (h_1); measure from the bottom of the air column to the oil meniscus, but not the thickened glass seal at the end of the tube. *Be careful that you do not knock the beaker off the wire gauze and ring when making your measurements!* Measure the temperature to the nearest 0.1 °C (t_1). (Record: 1.)

  c. Remove all of the ice from the beaker and then heat the water on the ring stand to a temperature that is 15–20 °C above the ice-water temperature. Stir the water periodically while it is heating. Stop heating when the thermometer reads about 5 °C below the desired temperature; the heat in the gauze and ring will cause the temperature to continue to rise. When the temperature has remained steady for several minutes, measure the lengths of the air columns and the temperature, as before. (Record: 2.)

  d. Repeat the heating process in Step 2c to obtain data at two more temperatures, each higher than the previous one by 15–20 °C. (Record: 3–4.) This will give you data at four temperatures in the range of approximately 0–60 °C.

3. Analyze the data.

  a. Convert each temperature to kelvins and record it in the appropriate column in the table.

  b. On your graph paper, choose a scale for the y-axis that begins at zero and spreads out the air column lengths (h) as much as possible. You will plot the temperatures on the x-axis; the values should range from about −300 °C to about +80 °C. Choose an appropriate scale that utilizes as much of the x-axis as possible. Plot *both* sets of h values versus temperature (in °C) using different colors or symbols to represent each set. Using a ruler, draw a straight line that best fits each set of four points obtained for each tube. Extend them to the left ("extrapolate") until they cross the x-axis. This value of x is your value for absolute zero. Calculate the percent error for the closer value, using −273.2 °C as the theoretical, or actual, value.

  c. Select the data from two different temperatures to use for verifying Charles's law; use points that are on or close to the line you've drawn. Using the mathematical expression for Charles's law, calculate the length that the trapped air *should* have at the higher of the two temperatures (T_a). This is the value for V_2 in the equation. *Show your work.* Compare this calculated value with your experimentally measured value. Find the percent error between the two values, using the calculated height of the air column as the theoretical value.

Data

Temperature in °C (t)	Length in cm (h)		Temperature in K (T)
	Tube 1	Tube 2	
1.			
2.			
3.			
4.			

Height of air column (in cm)

Charles's Law Plot

Temperature (°C)

Analysis

1. What is the percent error in your value for absolute zero? _____ %

$$\text{Percent error} = \frac{|\text{your value} - (-273.2 \text{ °C})|}{-273.2 \text{ °C}} \times 100\%$$

2. Which two data points did you choose to verify Charles's law? _____

   Record the values for those points (*a* represents the higher temperature and *b* the lower one).

   $T_a =$ _____ $T_b =$ _____

   $h_a =$ _____ $h_b =$ _____

   (experimental)

3. Calculate the theoretical value of h_a, using Charles's law and the values T_a, T_b, and h_b. (*Hint: Solve Charles's law, as modified for this experiment, $h_a/T_a = h_b/T_b$, to find h_a.*)

   $h_a =$ _____

   (theoretical)

$$\text{Percent error} = \frac{|\text{Experimental} - \text{Theoretical}|}{\text{Theoretical}} \times 100\%$$

4. What is the percent error between the theoretical and experimental values for h_a? _____ %

5. List several possible sources for error.

   incorrect or inaccurate reading of temperature or measurement of air column; measuring the air column too

   soon—before it has reached the temperature of the water bath; variable diameter of capillary tube; entire air

   column not submerged; graphing error

10B The Molar Mass of Oxygen

Prelab

Concepts

In 1808, Joseph L. Gay-Lussac formulated the law of combining volumes. He said that under equivalent conditions the volumes of reacting gases and their gaseous products can be expressed in small whole numbers. Although he did not know it at the time, the ratios of the small whole numbers are the same ratios that are expressed as coefficients of balanced equations.

This law of combining volumes later led Amedeo Avogadro to propose the following principle: under equivalent conditions, equal volumes of gases contain the same number of molecules. Experiments later determined just how many molecules were in a given volume. At STP, a volume of 22.4 L contains 6.022×10^{23} molecules, or 1 mole, of a gas. For this reason, 22.4 L is called the **molar volume of a gas**.

In this experiment, you will determine the *molar mass* of oxygen—that is, the mass of 1 mole (22.4 L) of oxygen. Then you will compare this experimental value to a theoretical value calculated from a balanced equation to determine your percent error.

Checkup

1. Define and give the value of the *molar volume of a gas*.

   the volume of 1 mole of gas at STP conditions; 22.4 L

2. Define *molar mass*.

   the mass of 1 mole of gas at STP conditions (which equals the

   mass of 22.4 L of that gas)

3. Under the same conditions, will the molar volumes of all gases be the same? will the molar masses? yes; no

4. Why does raising and lowering the beaker equalize the air pressure in the flask with that of the atmosphere?

   When the levels of the liquids in the flask and the beaker are at

   the same height or elevation, the same amount of atmosphere

   is above both of them; thus, the same pressure is above both

   of them.

5. Why do you siphon water back and forth between the beaker and the flask? to check for leaks

Procedure

1. Prepare the materials.

   a. Thoroughly clean and dry a large test tube. This will be your reaction tube.

Goals

✓ Measure the mass of oxygen produced in a chemical reaction.

✓ Measure the volume of the oxygen produced.

✓ Calculate the molar mass of oxygen, using the mass and volume of the oxygen produced.

✓ Compare the experimental value for the molar mass to a theoretical value (from a balanced equation) to determine a percent error.

Materials

balance
barometer
beaker, 250 mL
Bunsen burner
Erlenmeyer flask, 250 mL
graduated cylinder, 100 mL
iron (III) oxide (Fe_2O_3)
matches
pinchcock clamp
potassium chlorate ($KClO_3$)
ring stand
rubber stoppers, 1-hole and 2-hole
spatula
test tube clamp
test tube, large
thermometer
tubing, glass and rubber
weighing paper

You may wish to perform this experiment as a demonstration because it is so involved. If so, explain what you are doing in each step.

Be sure that the students have carefully read the Procedure section before the lab. It is very involved.

b. Determine the mass of the reaction tube. (Record: 1.)

c. On a piece of weighing paper, measure out about 0.1 g of iron (III) oxide (Fe_2O_3). Put this in the reaction tube. The Fe_2O_3 will act as a catalyst to help the $KClO_3$ release oxygen.

d. On another piece of weighing paper, measure out about 1.0 g of potassium chlorate ($KClO_3$). Add it to the iron (III) oxide in the reaction tube.

e. Determine the total mass of the mixture and the reaction tube. (Record: 2.)

f. Mix the Fe_2O_3 and $KClO_3$ thoroughly with a spatula, and then spread the mixture along about half the length of the reaction tube. Do not get it too near the open end of the tube.

g. Assemble the apparatus as shown in Figure 10B-1. Make sure that the bottom end of the reaction tube is lower than the mouth and that the water exit tube is ¼ in. from the bottom of the flask.

h. Fill the flask with water until the water level is just short of the gas inlet tube.

2. Make the apparatus leakproof.

a. Place about 50 mL of water in the 250 mL beaker.

b. Disconnect the reaction tube and remove the pinchcock clamp from the water exit tube.

c. Tip the flask about 90° to the right so that water can flow through the water exit tube to produce a siphon. The water will not siphon if there is a leak. (See Figure 10B-2.)

d. When the water exit tube has filled with water, set the flask down. At this point water should be siphoning from the flask.

e. Stop the siphoning by closing the water exit tube with the pinchcock clamp.

f. Now siphon the water back into the flask so that the water level is just short of the gas inlet tube in the flask. To do this, hold the beaker above the water level of the flask and remove the clamp. (See Figure 10B-3.)

g. As soon as the flask fills to the desired level, replace the clamp and put the beaker back on the desk.

h. Reconnect the reaction tube to the assembly.

i. Check all of the stoppers to be sure that they are inserted tightly.

j. Remove the clamp. The water level in the flask will fall slightly. After this change, the water level should remain at the new position.

10B-1   Oxygen generator

10B-2   Siphon from flask to beaker

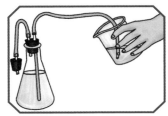

10B-3   Siphon from beaker to flask

Caution: If the mixture is too near the end of the tube, then it may come into contact with the rubber stopper, possibly causing an explosion when heated.

k. Equalize the air pressure in the flask with that of the atmosphere by raising or lowering the beaker until its water level is even with the level of water in the flask. Replace the clamp when the water levels in the beaker and flask are even. (See Figure 10B-4.)

l. Empty and dry the beaker and return it to the assembly.

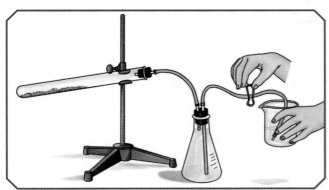

10B-4 Equalizing the pressure

3. Produce the oxygen gas.

a. *Remove the clamp* and slowly heat the mixture of Fe_2O_3 and $KClO_3$ near the middle of the test tube. Hold the burner in your hand and move the burner back and forth under the test tube. This will heat the mixture more uniformly. Gas will be produced from the chemical reaction, flow through the gas inlet tube, and force water into the beaker. Thus, the volume of water forced out of the flask into the beaker will be the volume of gas that was produced in the reaction. Note, however, that these are *not* STP conditions.

b. When the water has been displaced to within 1 in. of the bottom of the water exit tube, stop heating.

c. Without breaking any connections, allow the apparatus to stand until it cools to room temperature.

d. After the system has cooled to room temperature, raise or lower the beaker until the water levels in it and the flask are the same. When the two water levels are the same, replace the clamp.

e. Before you break any connections, as accurately as possible, measure the volume of water in the beaker with a 100 mL graduated cylinder. (Record: 3.) This is equivalent to V_1.

f. Since the temperature in the laboratory fluctuates considerably, the most accurate temperature for the oxygen from the reaction would be that of the water in the beaker. Determine the temperature of this water. (Record: 4.)

g. Carefully disconnect the reaction tube and determine its mass plus its contents. (Record: 5.)

h. Record the atmospheric pressure using a barometer. (Record: 6.)

You may want to take the atmospheric pressure reading and write it on the board for the entire class to see.

The students may have to interpolate between values on Table 10-4 in the text. Example: If the temperature is 62 °C, what is the vapor pressure of water?

TEMPERATURE (°C)	VAPOR PRESSURE (TORR)
60	149.38
62	unknown
65	187.54

$$\frac{62-60}{65-60} = \frac{unknown}{187.54-149.38}$$

$$\frac{2}{5} = \frac{unknown}{38.16}$$

$$unknown = 15.26$$

Therefore, the vapor pressure of water at 62 °C is 149.38 + 15.26, or 164.64 torr.

The correct answer for the molar mass of oxygen is 32.0 g/mol.

Data

1. Mass of reaction tube   ———— g
2. Mass of reaction tube plus mixture before heating   ———— g
3. Volume of water in beaker   ———— mL
4. Temperature of water in beaker   ———— °C
5. Mass of reaction tube plus mixture after heating   ———— g
6. Atmospheric pressure   ———— torr

Analysis

1. Determine the mass of the oxygen produced during heating.   ———— g

2. Determine the volume of the oxygen produced at STP.

   a. What is the partial pressure of oxygen? Use Table 10-4, pages 256, in your textbook to obtain the partial pressure of the water vapor. Then subtract the partial pressure of the water vapor from the atmospheric pressure to obtain the partial pressure of oxygen.   ———— torr

   b. What is the temperature of the oxygen in kelvins?   ———— K

   c. Substitute into the combined gas law the partial pressure of oxygen as P_1, the temperature (in K) of oxygen as T_1, the volume (in L) of oxygen produced as V_1, the STP pressure as P_2, and the STP temperature as T_2. Solve for V_2—the volume at STP.   ———— L

3. Divide the mass of evolved oxygen from Step 1 by the volume calculated in Step 2 (V_2) to get the number of grams per liter (g/L) of oxygen at STP.   ———— g/L

4. Derive the molar mass of oxygen at STP by multiplying the g/L from Step 3 by 22.4 L/mol.   ———— g/mol

5. Obtain the correct answer from your teacher.

   What is your percent error?   ———— %

11 Liquid Volume-Temperature Relationships

Prelab

Concepts

Based on kinetic molecular theory assumptions, you know that molecules move more rapidly as their average temperature increases. You would expect faster-moving molecules to occupy a greater volume. Since density is defined as mass divided by volume ($D = m/V$), and the mass of a given amount of matter does not change with temperature, you would expect the density of a given amount of matter to increase as the temperature decreased. If this trend continued as a liquid froze, the solid should be denser than the liquid because it occupies less space; the frozen substance should sink in its liquid. Water is an exception to this expectation due to the effects of hydrogen bonds and the unique structure of solid water. Ice has an open hexagonal structure, causing it to occupy more space as it freezes and become less dense.

In this lab, you will investigate the effect that temperature has on the volume of liquid water, and you will measure the volume change for water when it freezes. From this information, you will calculate the percentage change in volume when water freezes.

Checkup

1. Would you expect a chunk of solid alcohol to sink or float when it is placed in a container of liquid alcohol? Explain.

   It would sink because all substances except water are denser in

   their solid form than in their liquid form; a more dense sub-

   stance sinks in a less dense one.

2. Why do you need to find the volume of the water in the cylinder without the thermometer in it (Steps 8 and 11)?

   The thermometer occupies space when it is in the cylinder, but

   in order to do any density calculations for the water in the solid

   and liquid forms, you need to know the volume of the water

   only.

3. Explain why the volume of a liquid would be expected to be smaller at lower temperatures.

   The molecules move more slowly as their thermal energy de-

   creases (i.e., as the temperature decreases), thus effectively

   occupying less volume.

Goals

✓ Determine the effect of temperature on the volume and density of water.

✓ Measure the percent change in volume of liquid water when it freezes.

Materials

balance
beaker, 1000 mL
Bunsen burner
freezer
graduated cylinder, 100 mL, plastic
ice, crushed
iron ring
matches
plastic wrap (or Parafilm®)
ring stand
thermometer
wire gauze

Plastic cylinders are recommended here instead of glass ones to reduce breakage due to the expansion of freezing water. However, they generally cannot be read as accurately as glass cylinders. In a trial run of this lab, the glass cylinder used did not break when its contents were frozen solid. Another option, if both plastic and glass cylinders are available, is to use the glass ones for all but the freezing step and simply transfer the water from the glass to the plastic cylinder before placing it in the freezer.

It is best to consistently leave the thermometer in the cylinder while making temperature and volume measurements because of heat transfer and liquid loss if the thermometer is removed for each reading. Since these are all relative volume changes, the plot will have the same shape.

This will give the actual volume of the water *only* to serve as a reference for density and percent increase upon freezing.

The thermometer is removed to enable the calculation of the density of the hot water.

Procedure

1. Weigh your 100 mL graduated cylinder. (Record: 2.)

2. Obtain about 70 mL of water in your cylinder and weigh the total. (Record: 1.)

3. Fill your 1000 mL beaker about half to two-thirds full of crushed ice; add water to about the 1000 mL line. This should allow room for your graduated cylinder in the beaker.

4. Rest a thermometer on the bottom of the graduated cylinder and measure carefully the volume of water (plus thermometer) to 0.1 mL. (Record: 6a.) Also read the temperature to 0.1 °C. (Record: 6b.) Then place them together in the ice-water bath in the 1000 mL beaker. Be sure there is sufficient water in the beaker to be at a level that is higher than that in the graduated cylinder.

5. Carefully stir the water in the cylinder with the thermometer until it is 8–10 °C *lower* than room temperature. Again read the volume and temperature accurately with the thermometer resting on the bottom of the cylinder. (Record: 7.) You may need to remove the cylinder from the ice-water bath to make these measurements but do it *as quickly as possible* so as not to allow the water in the cylinder to warm.

6. Repeat the cooling and stirring procedure in Step 5, making your measurements at a temperature of 4–5 °C. (Record: 8.)

7. Allow the cylinder to remain in the ice-water bath until it has reached as low a temperature as possible (close to 0 °C). Make your measurements quickly, as before. (Record: 9.) This will give you 3 measurements that are below room temperature.

8. While the water is still close to 0 °C, take the thermometer out of the cylinder and again carefully measure the water volume *only* to 0.1 mL. (Record: 3.)

9. Now empty the ice water from your beaker and replace it with tap water to the same level. Set the beaker on the ring stand as you did in Lab 10A (Figure 10A-3) and begin heating the water with the burner off to one side of the beaker, not directly under the graduated cylinder. (This will help minimize "bumping," where pockets of vapor form under the base of the graduated cylinder.) As you heat the beaker, carefully stir the water in the graduated cylinder with the thermometer until it has reached a temperature that is about 20 °C higher than room temperature. *Be sure to stir sufficiently so that the contents of the cylinder are uniformly heated.* Remove the graduated cylinder from the beaker and quickly make your measurements, again with the thermometer in the cylinder. (Record: 10.)

10. Repeat the heating and measuring procedure in Step 9 in approximately 20-degree increments until the temperature is 80–85 °C. (Record: 11, 12.) This should give you 3 additional measurements that are above room temperature.

11. While it is still at its highest temperature, remove the thermometer from the cylinder and carefully read the volume of water only. (Record: 4.)

12. Turn off your burner and allow the apparatus to cool before you attempt to empty the hot water from it. Remove your thermometer from the cylinder and place a small piece of plastic wrap over the cylinder mouth to prevent loss of water by evaporation. Using a labeling method suggested by your teacher, label the graduated cylinder with your name and give it to your teacher to place in the freezer overnight. During the next class period, you will measure the volume of the frozen water in the cylinder. (Record: 5.)

13. On the graph provided, record your data points from the table by plotting the volume versus the temperature. Choose a scale that will spread out your data as much as possible. The y-axis will *not* start at zero! Start at a value one unit smaller than your smallest volume and end with a value that is the next higher integer than your largest value. The x-axis will go from 0–100 °C. Connect the points with a smooth curve.

14. Using your recorded data, perform the calculations and answer the questions in the Analysis section.

Data

1. Mass of graduated cylinder + water   <u>205.60</u> g

2. Mass of graduated cylinder   <u>136.40</u> g

3. Volume of water about 0 °C   <u>69.2</u> mL

4. Volume of hottest water   <u>72.2</u> mL

5. Volume of frozen water (ice)   <u>76.0</u> mL

	(a) Volume (mL)	(b) Temperature (°C)
6.	73.5	23.4
7.	73.0	11.0
8.	72.9	4.2
9.	73.0	1.0
10.	74.0	43.3
11.	74.8	63.3
12.	75.5	83.0

Analysis

1. What mass of water did you use in this experiment?   <u>69.20</u> g

2. What was the density of the liquid water at its lowest temperature? <u>69.20 g/69.2 mL = 1.00</u> g/mL

3. What was the density of the solid water (ice)? <u>69.20 g/76.0 mL = 0.911</u> g/mL

4. What can you say about the relative densities of liquid water and solid water?

   <u>Solid water is less dense than liquid water.</u>

5. By what percent did the volume change when the water froze? Compare the volume of liquid water at its lowest temperature to the volume of the ice. <u>[(76.0 mL − 69.2 mL)/69.2 mL] × 100% = +9.8%</u>

The data in these sections are sample data similar to what students might get. Their readings will vary from these depending on the mass of the different equipment used.

Volume versus Temperature

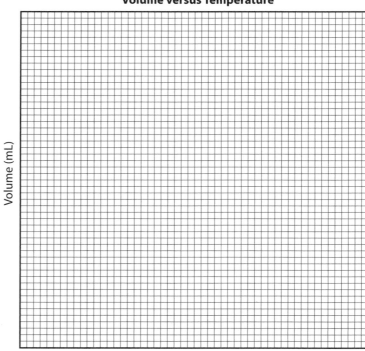

Volume (mL)

Temperature (°C)

6. Based on your answer to the previous question, should solid water float or sink in liquid water? Why?

    It should float because it is less dense.

7. From your graph, what can you say happens to the volume of liquid water as the temperature changes? Be specific in describing the relationship. ___The volume increases as the temperature increases.___

    _____

8. Calculate the density of the water at its highest temperature. _____ g/mL

9. Based on your answers to Analysis Questions 7–8, what happens to the density of liquid water as the temperature increases? ___The density of liquid water decreases as the temperature increases.___

    _____

10. By what percent did the volume of liquid water change over the range of your measurements? Use the smallest volume as the basis of comparison, i.e., as the denominator.

    [(75.5 mL – 72.9 mL)/72.9 mL] × 100% = +3.6%

12A Solubility Curve

Prelab

Concepts

The **solubility** of a solute is defined as the amount of solute that will dissolve in a given amount of solvent to make a saturated solution. However, the solubility of a substance is not constant—it varies with different conditions such as temperature. For example, the solubility of a solid dissolved in a liquid is often larger when the temperature is higher, but smaller when the temperature is lower. You can demonstrate this effect by allowing a hot salt solution to cool and then observing the temperature at which the solid begins to crystallize.

Checkup

1. Explain on a molecular basis why more table salt dissolves in hot water than in cold water. (See your text, Subsection 12.6.)

   Higher temperatures speed up molecular motion and thereby
   not only increase the number of collisions between solute and
   solvent particles but also provide the kinetic energy that most
   solids need in order to be broken apart into ions or individual
   molecules.

2. Define *solubility*.

   the amount of solute that will dissolve in a given amount of
   solvent at a given temperature to give a saturated solution

3. According to your text, what factors can affect the solubility of solid or gaseous solutes?

   temperature (both) and pressure (gases only)

4. What change will you observe that signals you to record the temperatures in this experiment?

   Crystals will begin to form.

5. Why will stirring help to dissolve the solute?

   A major factor that affects the rate at which a solute dissolves is
   the number of collisions that occur between the solute and
   solvent particles. Stirring increases the number of collisions by
   bringing more solvent in contact with the solute.

Procedure

1. Prepare the materials.

   a. Label four test tubes as follows: 4, 4.5, 5, and 5.5.

Goals

✓ Demonstrate how the solubility of a salt varies with temperature.

✓ Plot the solubility curve of a salt on the basis of observed data.

Materials

ammonium chloride (NH_4Cl)
balance
beaker, 250 mL
Bunsen burner
glass stirring rod
graduated cylinder, 10 mL
iron ring
matches
metric ruler
ring stand
test tube holder
test tubes, 4
thermometer
wire gauze

This is the reason that scientists must specify the exact conditions when measuring solubility.

b. Obtain 4.00 g of ammonium chloride; then add it to the test tube labeled "4." Repeat this step for 4.50 g, 5.00 g, and 5.50 g of ammonium chloride.

c. Add exactly 10.0 mL of water to each test tube.

d. Set up a hot-water bath, using a 250 mL beaker.

e. Place the four test tubes into the hot-water bath. Do not let any water from the beaker get into the test tubes; it is imperative that you not change the concentrations of the solutions.

2. Test the solubility versus temperature.

a. When the hot-water bath begins to boil, stir the solutions to help dissolve the ammonium chloride. (Be sure to rinse and dry your stirring rod before putting it into a different solution.) When the solute in all four tubes has completely dissolved, turn off the burner. The bath will remain hot for some time.

b. Using a test tube holder, remove test tube 5.5 from the water bath and place it in a test tube rack. Place a thermometer into the test tube and allow the solution to cool. You may periodically stir the solution gently with the thermometer.

c. Check the temperature at which crystallization occurs. (Record: 1.) Double-check this temperature by reheating the test tube *just enough* to dissolve the solute again. Recool the solution. (Record: 2.) If the temperature for the first and second crystallizations differs by more than a few degrees, carefully repeat the reheating and recooling process.

d. Repeat Steps 2b–c for the solutions containing 5.00, 4.50, and 4.00 g of ammonium chloride. *Note*: A cold-water bath may be needed to hasten the crystallization of the 4.00 g sample. (Record: 3–8.)

Data

1. Temperature for the first crystallization of the 5.50 g sample
   <u>70–72</u> °C

2. Temperature for the second crystallization of the 5.50 g sample
   <u>70–72</u> °C

3. Temperature for the first crystallization of the 5.00 g sample
   <u>56–59</u> °C

4. Temperature for the second crystallization of the 5.00 g sample
   <u>56–59</u> °C

5. Temperature for the first crystallization of the 4.50 g sample
   <u>45–47</u> °C

6. Temperature for the second crystallization of the 4.50 g sample
   <u>45–47</u> °C

7. Temperature for the first crystallization of the 4.00 g sample
   <u>27–30</u> °C

Remind the students to use distilled water for this procedure.

Answers will vary slightly but should be close to the temperatures given.

8. Temperature for the second crystallization of the 4.00 g sample

<u>27–30</u> °C

Analysis

1. On the following grid, plot the solubility curve for ammonium chloride from your data. If the temperatures for the first and the second crystallizations are not the same, plot their average value. Draw a smooth curve connecting the points. Extrapolate the curve to the temperature limits, using a dotted line.

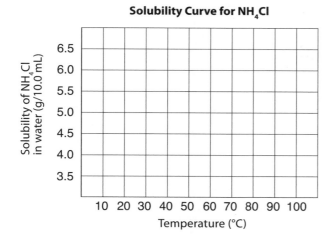

Solubility Curve for NH₄Cl

2. From your solubility curve, determine the solubility of ammonium chloride (in g/10.0 mL H_2O) at 60 °C. _____ g/10.0 mL H_2O

3. Obtain the accepted value for the solubility of ammonium chloride from your teacher. <u>5.52</u> g

4. Calculate your percent error. _____ %

5. Describe how the shape of the solubility curve would change, if at all, if your thermometer readings were all 4.5 °C lower than actual.

The shape would not change, but the entire curve would be shifted to the left of the actual curve, or to larger values for the solubility than actual.

12B Colligative Properties

Prelab

Concepts

As you learned in Section 12A of your text, when you add a solute to a solvent, a solution forms. Although a solution and its pure solvent may appear very similar, some of their properties differ. Boiling points, freezing points, vapor pressures, and osmotic pressures differ because they depend on the number of solute particles in solution. These properties that depend on the number of solute particles in solution—their concentration—and not on their identity are known as **colligative properties**. In this experiment, you will examine more closely two colligative properties—freezing point and osmotic pressure.

When you add a solute to a pure solvent, the solution freezes at a lower temperature. The amount by which the freezing point is lowered depends both on the concentration of the solute and on the solvent itself. For water, each mole of particles dissolved in 1 kg of water will lower the freezing point by 1.86 °C. For the solvent you will be using in this lab, t-butyl alcohol, each mole of particles in 1 kg of alcohol will lower the freezing point by 9.75 °C. These constants—1.86 °C and 9.75 °C—are known as **molal freezing-point constants**; they are represented by the symbol K_f and have units of °C/m, where m is the molal concentration (moles solute per kilogram solvent).

In this lab, you will use the following relationship to calculate the molar mass for a given solute:

$$\Delta T_f = K_f m$$

$$= K_f \left(\frac{\text{grams solute} \div \text{molar mass}}{\text{kg solvent}} \right). \qquad \textbf{Equation 1}$$

ΔT_f is the observed change in the freezing point for the solution compared to the pure solvent, K_f is the molal freezing-point constant for the solvent, and m is molality of the solution. If we rearrange the equation above for t-butyl alcohol, we derive the following equation:

$$\text{molar mass} = \frac{9.75\ °C/m \times \text{grams solute}}{\Delta T_f \times \text{kg solvent}}. \qquad \textbf{Equation 2}$$

From the direct relationship in Equation 1, you can see that the more concentrated the solution in solute particles, the larger the change in the freezing point will be and the lower the temperature at which it will freeze. Once you measure the change in freezing point, you will be able to calculate the molal concentration of the solution. Since you already know the masses of the solute and solvent that are present in the solution, you have all the information you need to calculate the molar mass of the solute. Equation 2 is in a form you can use to make the calculations directly.

In this lab, you will also demonstrate the movement of water through the semipermeable cell membrane of celery. From Subsection 12.17 of your text, you know that water flows from a more dilute solution into

Goals

✓ Measure the freezing-point depression of several solutions.

✓ Determine the molar mass of several substances, using their freezing-point depressions.

✓ Compare the experimental molar masses of several substances to their actual masses.

✓ Explore the effect of osmosis on celery when it is placed in water and in a salt solution.

Materials

antifreeze
balance
beakers, 150 mL, 2
beakers, 250 mL and 1000 mL
celery, two 1-inch pieces
copper wire stirrer
ethyl alcohol, absolute (optional)
glass stirring rod
ice, crushed
methyl alcohol
rubber stopper, size 00, split
sodium chloride (NaCl) solution, saturated
t-butyl alcohol (2-methyl-2-propanol)
test tubes, 3
thermometers, 2

Materials

Plastic dropper bottles for the antifreeze, methyl alcohol, and ethyl alcohol are advised. Since drop sizes vary, you may need to adjust the number of drops recommended in the lab.

Prepare the saturated salt solution ahead of time by stirring sodium chloride into the needed amount of water until no more will dissolve (approximately 36 g NaCl/100 mL solution). Decant the solution from the undissolved salt.

Pure, dry t-butyl alcohol will solidify near room temperature. Keep it in a warm bath during use.

a more concentrated solution—from the one with the smaller osmotic pressure into the one with the larger osmotic pressure. Depending on whether the solution into which the celery is placed is hypertonic or hypotonic compared to the solution inside the celery, water may flow either out of or into the celery, respectively. As a result, the celery will either lose mass and shrivel or gain mass and swell.

Checkup

1. Name and define the concentration unit that is generally used in colligative property problems.

   molality; moles solute per kilogram solvent

2. What would be the freezing-point depression in a solution containing 0.24 g ethyl alcohol (C_2H_5OH, 46.1 g/mol) in 5.68 g t-butyl alcohol? 8.9 °C

3. In this lab, what will you observe that indicates that the t-butyl alcohol is freezing?

   The liquid will become cloudy or slushy, indicating the formation of crystals.

4. Would the freezing point of a t-butyl alcohol solution containing 0.50 g methyl alcohol (32.1 g/mol) be lower than, higher than, or the same as the freezing point of a solution containing 0.50 g ethylene glycol (62.0 g/mol)? Explain your answer.

   It would be lower than that of the ethylene glycol solution because it contains more solute particles. Methyl alcohol has a smaller molar mass than ethylene glycol; thus, the same mass of each will contain more molecules of the less massive substance, depressing the freezing point to a greater extent.

5. Why must the equipment be dry in the freezing-point depression part of this lab?

   Water will act as a solute along with the added alcohol or glycol, causing error.

Procedure

1. Demonstrate osmosis.

   a. Obtain about 75 mL of saturated NaCl solution in a 150 mL beaker.

   b. Weigh each piece of celery on a balance. (Record: 1a–b.)

   c. Place one of the weighed celery pieces in the salt solution and the other in a second 150 mL beaker containing 75 mL of distilled water.

   d. Allow them to remain in their respective beakers until the end of the lab period (at least one hour).

   e. At the end of the period, remove the celery pieces from their beakers, rinse them in water, dry off excess water, and weigh them on the same balance you used in Step 1b. (Record: 2a–b.)

2. Demonstrate freezing-point depression.

   a. Place a thermometer and wire stirrer into one of your *dry* test tubes; weigh them on the balance, using the 250 mL beaker as a container for them. (Record: 3.) Fill your test tube about one-third full with *t*-butyl alcohol and weigh the assembly again. (Record: 4.) You should have about 5 g of the alcohol in the test tube.

   b. Assemble one thermometer, stirrer, and split stopper as shown in Figure 12B-1. If the alcohol solidifies (its normal freezing point is about 25 °C), melt it by holding it in your hand or by placing it in a *warm* water bath. Getting it too warm will slow the next step. Put about 600 mL of water in the 1000 mL beaker and adjust the temperature with small amounts of crushed ice, if necessary, so that it is no cooler than 20 °C. Use the second thermometer to monitor the temperature of the cool-water bath. Stir the water bath with a stirring rod so that the temperature stabilizes before you place the thermometer assembly into it. *The water bath that is used for determining the freezing points in this section should be no cooler than 5–6 °C cooler than the expected freezing point.* A bath that is too cool causes cooling to occur too rapidly and makes it more difficult to determine an accurate freezing point.

   c. Stir the contents of the test tube by moving the wire stirrer up and down rapidly; this helps reduce supercooling of the liquid. Observe the alcohol, carefully watching for cloudiness to appear; this indicates the appearance of crystals of solid alcohol and appears as sort of a slush. Note the temperature (to 0.1 °C) when the crystals first appear and the temperature has stabilized. (Record: 5.) Repeat this determination by warming the alcohol just until it is clear again and then replacing it in the cool-water bath.

   d. Remove the test tube assembly from the water bath and thoroughly dry the outside of the tube. Remove the rubber stopper to permit the addition of 8–9 drops (about 0.3 g) of antifreeze. Weigh the test tube, contents, wire stirrer, and thermometer on the same balance as in Step 2a. (Record: 6.) Add sufficient ice to the water bath to cool it to 10–15 °C. Repeat the freezing point

12B-1   Freezing-point assembly

determination explained in Step 2b, this time for the solution, noting the temperature (to 0.1 °C) at which you first see crystals (cloudiness) appear and when the temperature is stable. Do not mistake condensation appearing on the outside of the beaker for cloudiness within the test tube. Repeat this step, as before, by warming the solution in your hand until it clears and then refreezing it. Dry the thermometer and stirrer before using them in Step 2e.

e. Weigh your second *dry* test tube, stirrer, and thermometer in the 250 mL beaker. (Record: 8.) Add enough *t*-butyl alcohol to fill it one-third full and weigh it again, along with the stirrer and thermometer. (Record: 9.) Add 9–10 drops (about 0.15 g) of methyl alcohol and reweigh. (Record: 10.) Determine the freezing point of the solution as you did in Step 2d. (Record: 11.)

f. (*optional*) Repeat Step 2e, using 12–20 drops (0.2–0.3 g) of ethyl alcohol and your third *dry* test tube. Record your data in the appropriate blanks. (Record: 12–15.)

g. Pour all your alcohol solutions in the waste container provided.

Data

Osmosis

1. Mass of celery before osmosis
   a. distilled water   ——— g
   b. salt water   ——— g
2. Mass of celery after osmosis
   a. distilled water   ——— g
   b. salt water   ——— g

Freezing-point depression

3. Mass of assembly 1 and beaker   ——— g
4. Mass of assembly 1, beaker, and *t*-butyl alcohol   ——— g
5. Freezing point of *t*-butyl alcohol   ——— °C
6. Mass of assembly 1, beaker, *t*-butyl alcohol, and antifreeze   ——— g
7. Freezing point of antifreeze solution   ——— °C
8. Mass of assembly 2 and beaker   ——— g
9. Mass of assembly 2, beaker, and *t*-butyl alcohol   ——— g
10. Mass of assembly 2, beaker, *t*-butyl alcohol, and methyl alcohol   ——— g
11. Freezing point of methyl alcohol solution   ——— °C

(Steps 12–15 are optional.)
12. Mass of assembly 3 and beaker   ——— g
13. Mass of assembly 3, beaker, and *t*-butyl alcohol   ——— g

Check local regulations, but *t*-butyl alcohol is generally permissible in the sewer in small quantities (approximately 100 g) when flushed down the drain with plenty of water.

14. Mass of assembly 3, beaker, *t*-butyl alcohol, and
    ethyl alcohol _____ g

15. Freezing point of ethyl alcohol solution _____ °C

Analysis

Osmosis

1. Calculate the *change* in mass of each celery piece, using + or − in front of each mass.

   a. distilled water _____ g

   b. salt water _____ g

2. In which direction did water flow in each case—*into* or *out of* the celery?

   a. distilled water <u>into the celery</u>

   b. salt water <u>out of the celery</u>

3. Is the liquid *hypertonic* or *hypotonic* with respect to the celery?

   a. distilled water <u>hypotonic</u>

   b. salt water <u>hypertonic</u>

Freezing-point depression (Show your setups in the margin.)

4. Mass of *t*-butyl alcohol (assembly 1) _____ kg

5. Mass of antifreeze _____ g

6. ΔT_{f_1} _____ °C

7. Molar mass of antifreeze (ethylene glycol; Equation 2) _____ g/mol

8. Percent error (ethylene glycol = 62.1 g/mol) _____ %

9. Mass of *t*-butyl alcohol (assembly 2) _____ kg

10. Mass of methyl alcohol _____ g

11. ΔT_{f_2} _____ °C

12. Molar mass of methyl alcohol (Equation 2) _____ g/mol

13. Percent error (methyl alcohol = 32.0 g/mol) _____ %

14. Would your percent error for the molar mass be less, more, or the same if you had used a solvent that has a larger K_f, such as camphor (K_f = 40 °C/*m*)? Explain your answer.

    <u>It would be less. Percent error is relative to a standard, which is in the denominator; a larger denominator</u>

    <u>gives a smaller quotient.</u>

    (Steps 15–19 are optional.)

15. Mass of *t*-butyl alcohol (assembly 3) _____ kg

16. Mass of ethyl alcohol _____ g

17. ΔT_{f_3} _____ °C

18. Molar mass of ethyl alcohol (Equation 2) _____ g/mol

19. Percent error (ethyl alcohol = 46.1 g/mol) _____ %

Remind the students to use kilograms.

13A Molar Enthalphy of Fusion of Ice

Prelab

Concepts

As you learned in Chapter 13 of your text, if thermal energy is added to a solid at its melting point, its temperature will not change until the entire solid has melted. This additional thermal energy—*latent heat*—is being used to give the molecules sufficient energy to overcome the forces that hold them in their fixed positions in the crystal. During a phase change such as this, there is no temperature change. The thermal energy that is required to change a solid to a liquid at its melting point is known as the **molar enthalpy of fusion (ΔH_{fus})**, usually given in units of kJ/g. Water has a particularly large molar enthalpy of fusion, primarily due to the hydrogen bonding between molecules.

In this lab, you will determine the molar enthalpy of fusion of ice by using the law of energy conservation: energy is not lost in thermal energy transfers between matter. To simplify the calculations and procedure, we will assume that no thermal energy is liberated to or absorbed from the surroundings; only the ice and water will be considered. You will first calculate the thermal energy that is released when the temperature of a measured amount of hot water is cooled by a known amount. Ice will absorb this energy and melt to form water at its melting point, 0 °C. If sufficient thermal energy is available from the hot water, the temperature of this melted ice can now increase. Once thermal equilibrium is reached, the temperature of the melted ice and the water that was originally hot will be the same—equal to the final temperature of the mixture (t_{final}). Thus, the thermal energy "lost" by the hot water will equal the sum of the thermal energy needed to melt the ice and the thermal energy needed to warm the water. In word equation form,

thermal energy "lost" by hot water = thermal energy to melt ice
+ thermal energy gained by melted ice.

Equation 1

In cases where a substance is warmed but there is no phase change, according to the equation in your text,

$$\text{thermal energy } (Q) = mc_{sp}\Delta T,$$

where c_{sp} is the specific heat of a substance.

In order to make calculations less confusing and to always have positive values, in this lab we will find ΔT by subtracting the smaller from the larger value. If there is a phase change from solid to liquid, then no temperature change occurs and the equation is

$$Q = mass\Delta H_{fus}.$$

Let us make the following substitutions: c_w is the specific heat of water; Δt_{hot} is the difference between the initial and final temperatures of the hot water ($t_{initial} - t_{final}$); Δt_{cold} is the difference between the final temperature of the water and 0 °C ($t_{final} - 0$ °C); and $mass_{ice}$ is found from the difference between the final and initial volumes of water ($V_{final} - V_{initial}$). (Since the density of water is very close to 1.0 g/mL, the masses and volumes of water are essentially interchangeable.) Substituting these symbols for the words in Equation 1, we get

Goal

✓ Determine the heat of fusion of ice.

Materials

beaker, 250 mL
Bunsen burner
forceps *(optional)*
graduated cylinder, 100 mL
ice cubes
iron ring
matches
polystyrene cups, 8 oz, 3
ring stand
thermometer
towels, paper or cloth
wire gauze

$$(mass_{hot} \times c_w \times \Delta t_{hot}) = (mass_{ice} \times \Delta H_{fus}) + (mass_{ice} \times c_w \times \Delta t_{cold}).$$

Equation 2

Solving Equation 2 for the heat of fusion, we get

$$\Delta H_{fus} = [(mass_{hot} \times c_w \times \Delta t_{hot}) - (mass_{ice} \times c_w \times \Delta t_{cold})] \div mass_{ice}.$$

Equation 3

Checkup

1. What happens to thermal energy that is added to a solid at its melting point?

   It gives molecules the energy they need to overcome the forces

   that hold them in their fixed positions in the solid crystal.

2. Why does water have a relatively large molar enthalpy of fusion?

   There are hydrogen bonds between the molecules.

3. Why is it important to dry the ice before placing it into the hot water in the calorimeter?

   Water has a high specific heat, and it would absorb some of the

   thermal energy provided by the hot water instead of allowing

   that energy to be used to melt the ice.

4. Why do you not need to actually weigh the ice that is used in this experiment in order to know its mass?

   The increase in the volume of water will indicate the amount of

   melted ice. Because we know that water has a density of 1 g/mL,

   the number of additional mL equals the mass of the melted ice.

5. If a student obtained a value of 5.95 kJ/mol for his heat of molar enthalpy of fusion of ice, what is his percent error? (*Hints*: You have done this type of calculation in several previous labs; also see Analysis section in this lab.)

   The value would be off by 0.06 kJ/mol. This is a difference of 1%.

Procedure

1. Fill one of your polystyrene cups halfway with ice cubes and take it to your work station. Put the remaining two polystyrene cups one inside the other to make a nested cup calorimeter.

2. Clamp the iron ring to the ring stand and place a wire gauze on it. Fill the 250 mL beaker about half full of water, place it on the wire gauze on the ring stand, and heat it to 60–65 °C. Turn off your burner once the water is heated. Pour 30–35 mL of this hot water into the 100 mL graduated cylinder to preheat it. Wait about 30 seconds and pour the water out of the cylinder into the sink. Repeat this preheating process with another portion of hot water from your beaker.

3. Pour about 30 mL of your heated water into the preheated graduated cylinder and measure its volume to the nearest 0.1 mL. (Record: 1.) Transfer this hot water to the calorimeter and measure its temperature to the nearest 0.1 °C. (Record: 3.) Do this step and the remaining steps in each trial as quickly as possible to minimize thermal energy transfers between the calorimeter and the environment.

4. Dry off several ice cubes with a towel and immediately place them into the calorimeter, without splashing water out of it. Stir the ice-water mixture with the thermometer until either all the ice has melted or the temperature drops to a steady value that is close to zero. Measure this temperature to the nearest 0.1 °C. (Record: 4.)

5. Pour the water from the calorimeter into the graduated cylinder, being careful not to spill any. If there is any ice remaining, be careful to keep it out of the graduated cylinder; place a wire gauze over the top of the cup or the cylinder to help prevent this, or use forceps to remove the ice. Measure the volume of the water in the cylinder to 0.1 mL. (Record: 2.)

6. Repeat Steps 2–5, and record these results in the appropriate places in the column of the table labeled "Trial 2."

7. If your teacher instructs you to do so, or if your results from trials 1 and 2 are poor, you may need to do a third trial. If so, record your results under "Trial 3" in the table.

8. Perform the calculations in the Analysis section without help from your partner, using significant digits correctly. Show your setups where appropriate.

Data

	Trial		
	1	2	3 (optional)
1. $V_{initial}$ (hot water)	mL	mL	mL
2. V_{final} (total volume)	mL	mL	mL
3. $t_{initial}$ (hot water)	°C	°C	°C
4. t_{final} (final mixture)	°C	°C	°C

Analysis

The uppercase T designates the Kelvin temperature, while the lowercase t represents the Celsius readings. Because the size of a Celsius degree and a Kelvin are equal, we can substitute the temperature change without any conversion.

	Trial		
	1	**2**	**3 (optional)**
1. What was the mass of the hot water? (Assume 1.00 mL = 1.00 g.)	g	g	g
2. What was the temperature change of the hot water (Δt_{hot})?	°C	°C	°C
3. What volume of ice melted?	mL	mL	mL
4. What mass of ice melted?	g	g	g
5. What was the temperature change of the melted ice (Δt_{cold})?	°C	°C	°C
6. How many joules did the hot water transfer to the ice-water mixture? (Show setup.) $J = mass_{hot} \times c_w \times \Delta t_{hot}$	J	J	J
7. How many joules did the cold water absorb? (Show setup.) $J = mass_{ice} \times c_w \times \Delta t_{cold}$	J	J	J
8. How many total joules did the *ice* absorb? (answer for 6. – answer for 7.)	J	J	J
9. How many joules did *each gram* of ice absorb?	J/g	J/g	J/g
10. How many *kilojoules* would a *mole* of ice absorb? In other words, what is the molar enthalpy of fusion of ice? (1 mol H_2O = 18.02 g)	kJ/mol	kJ/mol	kJ/mol
11. What is your percent error? (actual value = 6.01 kJ/mol) (Show your work.)	%	%	%

12. List several possible sources of error in this experiment.

   Answers will vary but may include the following: the polystyrene cup absorbs some heat energy; heat

   is transferred to or from the surroundings; the graduated cylinder or thermometer may have been read

   inaccurately; all the ice may not have been at its melting point.

13B Specific Heat of a Metal

Prelab

Concepts

As you learned in Chapter 2 of your text, thermal energy is just one of several forms of energy, but the sum of all forms of energy is constant in any reaction or process. This observation is known as the **law of energy conservation**. Thus, as you are already aware from your experience, heat energy naturally "flows" between two objects that are in contact—from the one that has the higher temperature to the one that has the lower temperature—until they are both the same temperature. If this heat transfer occurs within an insulated container, known as a **calorimeter**, the surroundings lose or gain negligible amounts of heat energy during the transfer. Thus, the amount of heat energy "lost" by the hotter object will equal the amount of heat energy "gained" by the cooler object.

This assumption of energy conservation forms the basis for the lab you are about to perform. A known mass of a metal that has been heated to a measured temperature will be added to a known mass of water at a known cooler temperature. The amount of heat energy transferred (Q) is given by the equation

$$(Q) = mc_{sp}\Delta t \text{ (in °C)},$$

where m is the mass, c_{sp} is the specific heat, and Δt is the change in temperature of the object ($t_f - t_i$). Since the change in temperature has opposite signs for the two objects, the following relation holds:

$$-\text{heat lost}_{metal} = \text{heat gained}_{water}.$$

This can be rewritten as follows:

$$-(mc_{sp}\Delta t)_{metal} = (mc_{sp}\Delta t)_{water}.$$

Since the specific heat of water is known to be 4.18 J/g · °C, the only variable that is not known is the specific heat of the metal. Solving the equation above for the unknown, we can obtain the metal's specific heat:

$$c_{metal} = \frac{\left(mc_{sp}\Delta t\right)_{water}}{-\left(m\Delta t\right)_{metal}}.$$

Checkup

1. Upon what law is this lab based?

    the law of energy conservation

2. Why can we assume that negligible heat energy is transferred between the water and the surroundings in this experiment?

    An insulated cup—a calorimeter—will be used to minimize

    heat transfer.

3. Where does the heat energy lost by the hot metal end up?

    It raises the temperature of the water.

4. What is meant by the symbol Δt?

    It represents the change in temperature of the object, $t_f - t_i$.

Goal

✓ Determine the specific heat of a metal.

Materials

balance
beakers, 250 mL and 400 mL
Bunsen burner
cardboard, 4 × 4 in.
graduated cylinder, 100 mL
iron ring
matches
metal shot, 50–70 g
plastic wrap, approx. 1 × 1 in.
polystyrene cups, 6–8 oz, 2
ring stand
rubber stopper, 1-hole, #4, split
test tube holder
test tube, large
thermometer
wire gauze

Materials

Some 8 oz foam cups are tapered enough at the bottom that they can fit most of the way into a 250 mL beaker, making the 400 mL beaker unnecessary.

The zinc or copper metal shot from Lab 3B may be used here as well as any of a number of other metals.

Lowercase t is generally used for Celsius temperatures.

5. If 30.0 mL of water at 45.0 °C is added to an unknown amount of water at 10.0 °C, and the final temperature of the mixture is 30.0 °C, what is the mass of water that was at 10.0 °C?

$$(30.0 \text{ g})\left(\frac{4.18 \text{ J}}{\text{g} \cdot {}^\circ\text{C}}\right)(15.0 \text{ °C}) = (x)\left(\frac{4.18 \text{ J}}{\text{g} \cdot {}^\circ\text{C}}\right)(20.0 \text{ °C}); \ x = 22.5 \text{ g}$$

Procedure

1. Fill your 250 mL beaker halfway with water and place it on a wire gauze supported by an iron ring attached to your ring stand. Light the Bunsen burner and begin heating the water. While the water is heating, weigh your dry, large test tube and square of plastic wrap on the balance. (Record: 1.) Add enough dry metal shot to fill half of the test tube; weigh it again with the opening covered with the plastic wrap. (Record: 2.)

2. Place the covered test tube containing the metal shot into the beaker of water and bring the water to a boil. It is important to keep the plastic wrap over the end of the tube while it is heating in order to prevent water from getting inside the test tube. Allow the water to boil for several minutes before obtaining its temperature. Be sure the thermometer is not touching the sides or bottom of the beaker when you measure the temperature of the boiling water to 0.1 °C. Allow the test tube to remain in the boiling water for at least ten minutes. By that time, you can safely assume that the temperature of the metal shot is the same as that of the boiling water. This is the initial temperature of the metal. (Record: 3.)

3. While the metal sample is heating, weigh your two nested foam cups. (Record: 4.) Using your 100 mL graduated cylinder, measure about 50 mL of distilled water into the inner cup and weigh again. (Record: 5.) Place the nested cups into the 400 mL beaker to give them more stability. Insert the thermometer into the split rubber stopper, using a drop or two of liquid soap to lubricate it. Adjust the position of the stopper on the thermometer so that the bulb of the thermometer does not touch the bottom of the inner cup when it is inserted through the hole in the cardboard lid. (See Figure 13B-1 for the assembled setup.) Measure the initial temperature of the water in your foam cup calorimeter to 0.1 °C. (Record: 6.)

4. Using your test tube holder, remove the test tube from the boiling water, take off the plastic wrap, and quickly pour the metal into the calorimeter. *Be careful not to get any drops of hot water into the calorimeter or to splash water from the calorimeter when you pour in the metal shot!* Cover it with the cardboard lid and stir the mixture carefully with your thermometer. Note the temperature of the water about every 30 seconds and record the highest temperature reached. (Record: 7.) This is the final temperature of both the metal and the water.

5. Carefully decant into the sink as much water as possible without losing any metal shot. Pour the wet metal shot into the designated container so it can be dried and reused.

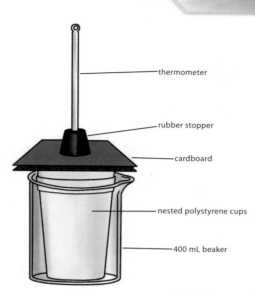

thermometer

rubber stopper

cardboard

nested polystyrene cups

400 mL beaker

13B-1 Foam cup calorimeter

Data

1. Mass of test tube and plastic wrap   ———— g

2. Mass of test tube, plastic wrap, and metal   ———— g

3. Temperature of boiling water (t_i for metal)   ———— °C

4. Mass of cups   ———— g

5. Mass of cups and water   ———— g

6. Temperature of water in cups (t_i for water)   ———— °C

7. Temperature of water and metal (t_f for both)   ———— °C

Analysis

1. What mass of metal shot did you use?   ———— g

2. What mass of water was in the calorimeter?   ———— g

3. Calculate Δt for the *metal*. ($\Delta t = t_f - t_i$)   ———— °C

4. Calculate Δt for the *water*. ($\Delta t = t_f - t_i$)   ———— °C

5. Using the equation and information given in the Concepts section of this lab, calculate the metal's specific heat.

————————————————— J/g · °C *(Show your work and use significant digits correctly!)*

6. Using the actual value for the specific heat of the metal supplied by your teacher, calculate the percent error in your experimental value.   _____ %

7. List at least three possible sources of error in your experiment.

   loss of heat energy in the transfer of metal to calorimeter; loss of heat energy to the surroundings (e.g., the

   foam cup); insufficient heating of the metal; inaccurate reading of the thermometer; loss of water from the

   calorimeter; transfer of hot water into the calorimeter

8. Would the following errors make the experimental specific heat of the metal larger or smaller, or would they have no effect? Why?

   a. Some hot metal spilled onto the table during its transfer into the calorimeter.

      Smaller; Δt_{water} is too small.

   b. The thermometer readings were all in error by being 2.3 °C higher than the actual temperature.

      No effect; the error subtracts out.

   c. The recorded mass of the water in the cup was too large.

      Larger; m_{water} is too large.

13C Enthalpies of Solution and Reaction

Prelab

Concepts

Solution processes, chemical reactions, and phase changes are all processes that absorb or release energy. This energy is often in the form of thermal energy, which has units of joules (J). Remember that the **joule** is the standard metric system (SI) unit of measurement for energy and work and is related to the calorie by the definition 1 cal = 4.184 J. (A calorie is the amount of thermal energy required to raise the temperature of 1 g of water by 1 °C.) If you divide the number of joules liberated or absorbed by the number of moles involved in a process, you can express the enthalpy change (ΔH), or heat content change, of that process. The units are J/mol, and, in our textbook as well as many others, tables express them as kJ/mol.

Scientists use the water environment of a calorimeter to measure the thermal energy liberated or absorbed in a process or reaction. If a process liberates thermal energy, it will cause an increase in the temperature of the water. If it absorbs thermal energy, it will cause a decrease in the temperature of the water. The formula for calculating the amount of thermal energy absorbed or released by a process is this:

$$\text{joules} = m_{water} \text{ (in g)} \times \Delta t \text{ (in °C)} \times c_{water}.$$

To find the mass of water in this equation, you must first know how many milliliters of aqueous (water) solution are involved in the process. Then, using the density of water (1.00 g/mL), you can convert milliliters to grams. (Since these are dilute solutions, it is sufficiently accurate for our purposes to assume that the density of the solution is the same as the density of the solvent, water.) For example, in the reaction between HCl and NaOH, you will use 50.0 mL of HCl and 35.0 mL of NaOH. This adds up to 85.0 mL of solution, or 85.0 g of water. When you substitute the 85.0 g into the formula along with the values for temperature change and specific heat, you can calculate the number of joules. Remember, this calculation does not yield the enthalpy change. To find ΔH, you must perform two more steps—divide by the number of moles, and convert J to kJ—giving the proper units, kJ/mol.

Scientists use an experimental procedure similar to this one to determine the enthalpy change values found in textbook tables. With these values and a balanced equation, you can predict the theoretical enthalpy change for a process. The formula for determining a standard enthalpy change is this:

$$\Delta H° = \Sigma \Delta H°_{f \text{(products)}} - \Sigma \Delta H°_{f \text{(reactants)}}.$$

Whether you determine the change in enthalpy by this experimental procedure or from textbook tables, a negative ΔH indicates an exothermic process and a positive ΔH indicates an endothermic process. An exothermic process releases energy to the surroundings; temperature therefore increases. An endothermic process absorbs energy from the surroundings; temperature therefore decreases.

Goals

✓ Determine the enthalpy change for a solution process.

✓ Determine the enthalpy changes for two chemical reactions.

Materials

balance
cardboard, 4 × 4 in.
graduated cylinder, 100 mL
hydrochloric acid (HCl), 1.00 *M*
magnesium ribbon, 0.10–0.15 g
paper towel
polystyrene cups, 2
potassium nitrate (KNO_3), solid
ring stand
sandpaper
sodium hydroxide (NaOH), 1.00 *M*
test tube clamp
thermometer
weighing paper

The symbol Δt represents the change in temperature of the water, $t_1 - t_2$, and c_{water} is 4.184 J/(g · °C).

This calculation assumes that no thermal energy is lost or gained by the calorimeter during the experiment. Also, since the specific heat for water is 4.184 J/(g · °C), the change in enthalpy (ΔH) will be in J/mol. If the enthalpies are large, you can convert J/mol to kJ/mol.

Checkup

1. According to the text, what use is made of the *joule*?

   It is the SI unit used to measure work and any kind of energy.

2. What are the two ways of determining enthalpy changes mentioned in the Concepts section of this experiment?

   experimentally, using a calorimeter; theoretically, using a

   balanced equation

3. What will be used as the calorimeter in this experiment?

   two polystyrene cups

4. What type of process does a negative ΔH indicate—endothermic or exothermic?

   an exothermic process

5. Do the products or the reactants have more energy in an endothermic process?

   The products have more energy in an endothermic reaction.

Procedure

Prepare the calorimeters. Assemble two polystyrene cups and a thermometer as shown in Figure 13C-1. Your teacher may ask you to perform each part of the experiment twice.

Part A: A Solution Process

1. Measure 50.0 mL of water with a large graduated cylinder. Pour this water into the inner polystyrene cup.

2. Determine the temperature of this water to the nearest 0.1 °C. (Record: Part A1.) Be sure the thermometer bulb is completely submerged in the water.

3. Determine the mass of a piece of weighing paper. (Record: Part A2.) While the weighing paper is still on the balance, add 3 to 4 g of KNO_3. Determine this mass. (Record: Part A3.)

4. Add the KNO_3 to the water, cover your calorimeter with the cardboard lid, and begin swirling the cups gently, while closely observing the temperature. Watch for the lowest temperature reached over a period of several minutes and record it to the nearest 0.1 °C. (Record: Part A4.)

Part B: A Reaction Process

1. Empty your calorimeter, rinse it, and allow the excess water to drain from your cup.

2. Accurately measure 50.0 mL of 1.00 *M* HCl solution with a large, dry graduated cylinder and pour this into the inner cup.

3. Record the temperature of the HCl solution to the nearest 0.1 °C. (Record: Part B1.)

4. Rinse your graduated cylinder and measure accurately 35.0 mL of 1.00 *M* NaOH solution.

13C-1 Foam cup calorimeter

Lids with holes for the thermometers dramatically decrease the energy loss, producing more accurate results.

Although the solution process is not a type of reaction, heat is given off or released as a solution is formed.

Remind the students to use distilled water for these procedures.

This is a neutralization process.

The concentrations of the acid and base should be as close to 1.00 *M* as possible for the best results. Both solutions should also be at the same temperature.

5. Add the NaOH solution, all at one time, to the HCl in the cup, and then cover.

6. While gently swirling the cup, closely observe the temperature over a period of several minutes. Record the highest temperature reached to the nearest 0.1 °C. (Record: Part B2.)

Part C: A Reaction Process

1. Empty your calorimeter, rinse it well with water, and let it drain.

2. Measure 75.0 mL of 1.00 M HCl solution and pour it into the inner cup.

3. Measure the temperature of the HCl in the cup to the nearest 0.1 °C. (Record: Part C1.)

4. Obtain a piece of magnesium ribbon that has a mass between 0.10 and 0.15 g. Clean the magnesium ribbon with sandpaper, and then wipe it with a clean paper towel.

5. Determine the mass of the clean metal to the nearest 0.01 g. (Record: Part C2.)

6. Roll the magnesium ribbon into a loose ball, drop it into the acid, and cover the cup. While gently swirling the cup, observe the temperature constantly until all the metal has dissolved, plus a few additional minutes. Record the highest temperature reached to the nearest 0.1 °C. (Record: Part C3.)

Data

Part A: The Change in Enthalpy for a Solution

	Trial 1	Trial 2
1. Initial temperature of water	_____ °C	_____ °C
2. Mass of weighing paper	_____ g	_____ g
3. Mass of weighing paper and KNO$_3$	_____ g	_____ g
4. Final temperature of the KNO$_3$ and water solution	_____ °C	_____ °C

Part B: The Change in Enthalpy for a Reaction

	Trial 1	Trial 2
1. Initial temperature of HCl solution	_____ °C	_____ °C
2. Final temperature of HCl and NaOH reaction	_____ °C	_____ °C

Part C: The Change in Enthalpy for a Reaction

	Trial 1	Trial 2
1. Initial temperature of HCl solution	_____ °C	_____ °C
2. Mass of clean magnesium ribbon	_____ g	_____ g
3. Final temperature of HCl and magnesium ribbon reaction	_____ °C	_____ °C

This is a redox reaction.

The surface of the magnesium ribbon is somewhat oxidized. The sandpaper will remove the oxidized layer.

Analysis

Part A: The Change in Enthalpy for a Solution

Since ΔH_{soln} is expressed as J/mol (or kJ/mol), you must calculate the joules and the moles and then divide those answers to get J/mol.

1. Calculate the joules. Be sure to use the proper sign (+ or −). _____ J
   joules = $m_{water}\Delta t c_{water}$

2. Calculate the moles of KNO_3.
   a. How many grams of KNO_3 dissolved? _____ g
   b. How many moles of KNO_3 dissolved? _____ mol

3. Calculate the kilojoules per mole. (*Note*: Divide the number of joules calculated in Step 1 by the number of moles calculated in Step 2. Then divide the result by 1000 to convert joules to kilojoules.) _____ kJ/mol

4. Obtain the theoretical value from your teacher for this reaction and calculate your percent error. _____ %

5. Was the formation of the solution an exothermic or an endothermic process? <u>endothermic</u>

Part B: The Change in Enthalpy for a Reaction

1. Calculate the joules. Be sure to use the proper sign (+ or −). _____ J
   joules = $m_{water}\Delta t c_{water}$

2. Calculate the moles of NaOH used (the limiting reactant). (*Hint*: Use the volume of NaOH reacted and the molarity, M, of NaOH to calculate the number of moles.) <u>0.0350 L × 1.00 mol/L = 0.0350</u> mol

3. Calculate the kilojoules per mole. _____ kJ/mol

4. Obtain the theoretical value from your teacher for this reaction and calculate your percent error. _____ %

5. Was the reaction exothermic or endothermic? <u>exothermic</u>

Part C: The Change in Enthalpy for a Reaction

1. Calculate the joules. Be sure to use the proper sign (+ or −). _____ J
   joules = $m_{water}\Delta t c_{water}$

2. Calculate the moles of Mg reacted.
   a. How many grams of magnesium ribbon reacted? _____ g
   b. How many moles of magnesium ribbon reacted? _____ mol

3. Calculate the kilojoules per mole. _____ kJ/mol

4. Was the reaction exothermic or endothermic? <u>exothermic</u>

5. Using handbook values of −166.9 kJ/mol and −796.9 kJ/mol for the ΔH°_f of HCl (*aq*) and $MgCl_2$ (*aq*), respectively, calculate the theoretical ΔH° for this reaction. _____ kJ

   <u>[(−796.9 kJ/mol)(1 mol)] − [(−166.9 kJ/mol)(2 mol)] = −463.1 kJ</u>

6. Calculate your percent error. _____ %

The theoretical value is +34.89 kJ/mol. Do not expect completely accurate results. Experimental error of 2 to 5 percent can be expected because of inaccurate measurements and energy loss (or gain).

The theoretical value for the neutralization reaction is −57.7 kJ/mol.

14 Reaction Rates

Prelab

Concepts

The **rate of a chemical reaction** is the speed at which a chemical reaction proceeds. It can also be defined as either the amount of product formed per unit of time or the amount of reactant consumed per unit of time. You can alter the rate of a reaction by changing either the number of collisions between molecules or the force of their collisions. Concentration, temperature, pressure, catalysts, and the nature of the reactants themselves are all factors that can affect reaction rates.

In this experiment, you will change the rate of a reaction by altering the concentration and the temperature. You will observe how the reaction rate depends on concentration when you keep the temperature and the concentration of one reactant constant while varying the concentration of the other reactant. You will also observe the effect of temperature on reaction rate when you keep both reactant concentrations constant while varying the temperature.

The reaction you will use is the decomposition of the thiosulfate ion, $S_2O_3^{2-}$, supplied by the compound sodium thiosulfate, $Na_2S_2O_3$. The thiosulfate ion decomposes in the presence of acid to form sulfur and sulfurous acid as shown in the equation

$$S_2O_3^{2-} (aq) + 2H^+ (aq) \longrightarrow S (s) + H_2SO_3 (aq).$$

When the sulfur forms, the solution will turn cloudy. Thus, when you measure the time from the moment the reactants are mixed to the point when the solution turns cloudy (when sulfur forms), you are measuring the time required for this decomposition reaction.

Checkup

1. Define *rate of a chemical reaction*.

   It is the speed at which a chemical reaction proceeds, the

   amount of reactant used per unit of time, or the amount of

   product formed per unit of time.

2. What two factors will you test in this experiment?

   concentration and temperature

3. On a molecular basis, how do the factors listed in the first paragraph above affect the rate of a reaction?

   They increase or decrease either the number of collisions be-

   tween molecules or the force of those collisions.

4. How many samples of stock solution will you prepare in Part A of the procedure? five

5. How will you be able to tell when the reactions are completed?

   The solutions will turn cloudy and become opaque.

Goals

✓ Observe factors that affect reaction rates.

✓ Determine the concentration of an unknown on the basis of its reaction rate.

Materials

beakers, 150 mL and 250 mL

black marker

buret clamp

burets, 2

graduated cylinder, 10 mL

hydrochloric acid (HCl), 1.0 *M*

ice

ring stand

sodium thiosulfate ($Na_2S_2O_3$), 0.10 *M*

test tube rack

test tubes, 10

thermometer

watch with second hand

6. How is the rate of a reaction related to the time that it takes it to occur? <u>Rate and time are inversely related. Reactions with</u>

<u>high rates require short time periods to occur.</u>

Procedure

Part A: Measuring the Effect of Concentration on Reaction Rates

1. Prepare the materials.

a. Obtain two burets and one clamp. Fill one buret with 0.10 M $Na_2S_2O_3$ and fill another with distilled water. Place the burets in the clamp. (See Figure 16B-1, Lab 16B for the setup.)

b. Drain a little liquid from each buret to fill their tips. Stop when the water level reaches the 0 mL mark.

c. Place ten clean test tubes (five per row) in a test tube rack. Be sure they have no residual water in them.

d. Use a graduated cylinder to add 5.0 mL of 1.0 M HCl to each test tube in one row. *Measure accurately!* Label the test tubes in the other row from 1 to 5.

e. Prepare mixtures (stock solutions) of 0.10 M $Na_2S_2O_3$ and water in the remaining test tubes according to the following proportions:

	Stock Solution	
Test Tube Number	Volume of 0.10 M $Na_2S_2O_3$ (mL)	Volume of H_2O (mL)
1	5.0	0.0
2	4.0	1.0
3	3.0	2.0
4	2.0	3.0
5	1.0	4.0

f. Using a black marker, make an X about ¼" high on a piece of white paper.

2. Measure the rates of reaction.

a. Mix the contents of test tube 1 with one of the test tubes of HCl. Begin timing the reaction as soon as the reactants are mixed. Pour the mixture from one test tube to the other four times to ensure even mixing. Rest the bottom of the tube containing the mixture over the black X you drew in Step 1f. Observe the X by looking down through the tube. When the cloudiness is sufficient to make the X disappear, record the elapsed time. (Record: Part A1.)

b. Repeat Step 2a for test tubes 2, 3, 4, and 5. (Record: Parts A2–5.)

Measurements could be made with pipets or graduated cylinders rather than burets, but burets are quicker and more accurate.

Remind the students to use distilled water for this procedure.

When solutions of the thiosulfate ion and the acid are first mixed, nothing seems to happen. Eventually, the solution will turn cloudy as sulfur forms. (The sulfur is a colloidal precipitate.) The rate of reaction will be the amount of time required for the thiosulfate ion to be used up. There is less subjectivity in determining the end of the reaction by watching for the *disappearance* of an object rather than for the *beginning* of cloudiness.

3. Obtain a 5.0 mL sample of a solution of $Na_2S_2O_3$ of unknown molarity. Measure the time it takes for this solution to become cloudy when mixed with 5.0 mL of 1.0 M HCl. (Record: Part A6.)

Part B: Measuring the Effect of Temperature on Reaction Rates

1. Prepare the materials.

   a. Obtain six test tubes. Be sure they are clean and drained of observable amounts of water.

   b. Put 5.0 mL of 1.0 M HCl in each of three test tubes labeled "HCl."

   c. Put 5.0 mL of 0.10 M $Na_2S_2O_3$ in each of three test tubes labeled "$Na_2S_2O_3$."

2. Measure the rate of a reaction at room temperature.

   a. Mix a test tube of HCl with a test tube of $Na_2S_2O_3$ by pouring the contents from one test tube to the other four times. Begin timing the reaction as soon as the reactants are mixed. When you can no longer see the X while looking through the solution, stop your timing. Record the elapsed time. (Record: Part B1.)

   b. Measure the room temperature. (Record: Part B2.) This is the temperature of the environment of the first reaction.

3. Measure the rate of a reaction in warm water.

   a. Prepare a warm-water bath of approximately 35 °C in a 250 mL beaker by mixing hot and cold tap water.

   b. Put a test tube of HCl and a test tube of $Na_2S_2O_3$ in the warm-water bath.

   c. After five minutes, mix the two test tubes by pouring the contents from one test tube to the other four times. Begin timing the reaction as soon as the reactants are mixed. After mixing, put the test tube containing the mixture back into the water bath and put the paper with the black X underneath it. Again, stop timing when the black X disappears as a result of the cloudiness. (Record: Part B3.)

   d. Measure the temperature of the warm-water bath. This is the temperature of the environment of the second reaction. (Record: Part B4.)

4. Measure the rate of a reaction in cold water.

   a. Prepare a cold-water bath of approximately 10 °C in a 150 mL beaker by mixing ice and cold tap water.

   b. Put the remaining test tubes of HCl and $Na_2S_2O_3$ into the cold-water bath.

   c. Repeat Steps 3c–d for the test tubes in the cold-water bath. Record the time and temperature. (Record: Parts B5–6.)

Have a buret at the front of the room with the unknown concentration of $Na_2S_2O_3$. Make this unknown by mixing 5.5 parts $Na_2S_2O_3$ (for example, 55 mL) with 4.5 parts H_2O (for example, 45 mL).

Students can save time if they prepare their hot- and cold-water baths at this point.

Data

Part A: Effect of Concentration on Reaction Rate

1. Elapsed time for mixture in test tube 1 _____ s

2. Elapsed time for mixture in test tube 2 _____ s

3. Elapsed time for mixture in test tube 3 _____ s

4. Elapsed time for mixture in test tube 4 _____ s

5. Elapsed time for mixture in test tube 5 _____ s

6. Elapsed time for the unknown concentration
   of $Na_2S_2O_3$ _____ s

Part B: Effect of Temperature on Reaction Rate

1. Elapsed time for mixture at room
   temperature _____ s

2. Room temperature _____ °C

3. Elapsed time for the warm mixture _____ s

4. Temperature of the warm mixture _____ °C

5. Elapsed time for the cold mixture _____ s

6. Temperature of the cold mixture _____ °C

Analysis

1. Plot the time required for each reaction versus the thiosulfate ion concentration.

   a. Calculate the concentration of the thiosulfate ion, $S_2O_3^{2-}$, for all five reactions in Procedure Part A, Step 1. The values for the first reaction have been calculated for you. You can calculate the moles of $S_2O_3^{2-}$ by using the following method:

   $$\frac{5.0 \text{ mL } Na_2S_2O_3}{} \left| \frac{1 \text{ L}}{1000 \text{ mL}} \right| \frac{0.10 \text{ mol } S_2O_3^{2-}}{1 \text{ L}} = 0.00050 \text{ mol } S_2O.$$

   Then calculate the concentration of the $S_2O_3^{2-}$ ion, using the following method:

   $$\frac{0.00050 \text{ mol } S_2O_3^{2-}}{10.0 \text{ mL}} \left| \frac{1000 \text{ mL}}{1 \text{ L}} \right. = 0.050 \text{ } M \text{ } S_2O_3^{2-}.$$

   Complete the remainder of the chart.

Test Tube Number	Volume of $Na_2S_2O_3$ (mL)	Volume of H_2O (mL)	Volume of 1.0 M HCl (mL)	Total Volume (mL)	Moles of $S_2O_3^{2-}$	Molarity of $S_2O_3^{2-}$
1	5.0	0.0	5.0	10.0	0.00050	0.050
2	4.0	1.0	5.0	10.0	0.00040	0.040
3	3.0	2.0	5.0	10.0	0.00030	0.030
4	2.0	3.0	5.0	10.0	0.00020	0.020
5	1.0	4.0	5.0	10.0	0.00010	0.010

b. Now make a graph on the following grid. Plot the time for each reaction on the *y*-axis and the concentration of the thiosulfate ion on the *x*-axis. Draw a smooth curve through the points.

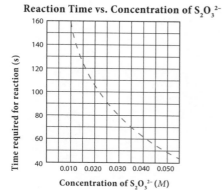

Reaction Time vs. Concentration of S$_2$O$_3^{2-}$

Time required for reaction (s) — *y*-axis

Concentration of S$_2$O$_3^{2-}$ (*M*) — *x*-axis

c. How does the *rate* of the reaction vary with the concentration of the thiosulfate ion?

As the concentration increases, the reaction rate increases.

d. Using your graph, estimate the concentration of thiosulfate in your unknown solution.

Answers should be consistent with graphs; about 0.028 *M*.

2. Plot the reaction *rate* versus the temperature.

a. Now graph the time required for the reaction on the *y*-axis and the temperature on the *x*-axis on the following grid. Draw a smooth curve through the points.

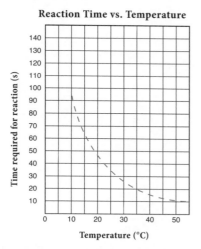

Reaction Time vs. Temperature

Time required for reaction (s) — *y*-axis

Temperature (°C) — *x*-axis

For both graphs, the students' data points may vary somewhat, but the curves should have this same basic shape.

b. How does the rate of a reaction change when temperature increases?

As temperature increases, the reaction rate increases.

c. Using your graph, predict how long it would take for a reaction to occur at 0 °C and at 50 °C.

Answers must be consistent with the data from the students' graphs.

15 Chemical Equilibrium

Prelab

Concepts

Many reactions are reversible. That is, a forward reaction forms products at the same time that a reverse reaction re-forms reactants. The forward reaction has its greatest rate at the beginning, and then it gradually slows down as the reactants are being consumed. On the other hand, the reverse reaction is extremely slow in the beginning, but as the concentration of the products increases, it becomes faster and faster. Eventually the rate of the forward reaction equals the rate of the reverse reaction, and **equilibrium** is established. (See Figure 15-1.) Since both reactions are now proceeding at the same rate, the concentration of each type of ion or molecule remains constant.

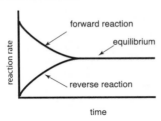

15-1   Equilibrium

There are three important stresses that affect an equilibrium: a change in concentration, a change in pressure (gases only), and a change in temperature. According to Le Châtelier's principle, an equilibrium will shift to relieve the effect of the stress. In this experiment, you will demonstrate Le Châtelier's principle by changing the concentration of the ions and by changing the temperature for the following equilibrium:

$$\underset{\text{pale yellow}}{FeCl_3} + \underset{\text{colorless}}{3KSCN} \rightleftharpoons \underset{\text{red}}{Fe(SCN)_3} + \underset{\text{colorless}}{3KCl}.$$

For example, adding more iron (III) chloride increases the number of collisions between reactant particles. This initially increases the rate of the forward reaction, followed by a decrease in the rate as the reactants are being consumed. This process would be observed by the change in color from yellow to red and indicated in the equation by the larger arrow toward the right:

$$FeCl_3 + 3KSCN \rightleftharpoons Fe(SCN)_3 + 3KCl.$$

The reverse reaction simultaneously increases as a result of the increasing concentration of products. When the two rates are equal, equilibrium is once more established. At the new equilibrium, however, the rates of both reactions are greater than they were in the original equilibrium. (See Figure 15-2.)

Goal

✓ Observe the direction in which the equilibrium shifts when the concentration of each reaction component is changed.

Materials

beakers, 150 mL and 250 mL
Bunsen burner
Erlenmeyer flask, 250 mL
iron (III) chloride ($FeCl_3$), 0.25 M
matches
potassium chloride (KCl), solid
potassium thiocyanate (KSCN), 0.25 M
rubber stopper
test tube holder
test tube rack
test tubes, 5
transfer pipets

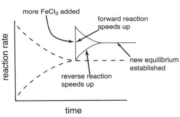

original (- - -) and new (——) equilibrium

15-2   New equilibrium

The red color is actually due to the formation of the complex ion, $Fe(SCN)^{2+}$, more correctly written $Fe(H_2O)_5(SCN)^{2+}$. However, this need not concern us here.

Checkup

1. Define *equilibrium*.

   the point in a reaction at which the rate of the forward reaction

   equals the rate of the reverse reaction

2. What happens to the concentration of ions when the solution is at equilibrium?

   The concentration of each ion stays the same.

3. What stresses can affect an equilibrium?

   changes in temperature, pressure, and concentration

4. What is Le Châtelier's principle?

   Le Châtelier's principle states that a stress will shift an equilib-

   rium in the direction that relieves the effect of the stress.

5. Explain what is meant by the phrase "the equilibrium is shifted forward."

   Since more products form as a result of additional reactants,

   the equilibrium is said to have shifted to the products—from

   left to right, or forward—as the reaction is written.

Procedure

1. Obtain approximately 3 mL of iron (III) chloride solution and 3 mL of potassium thiocyanate solution in separate labeled beakers. Throughout this experiment, make sure that you do not contaminate these solutions with each other.

2. Using separate pipets, add twenty drops of the iron (III) chloride solution and twenty drops of the potassium thiocyanate solution to 100 mL of water in a 250 mL Erlenmeyer flask. Mix thoroughly by swirling the contents, and note the color. (Record: 1.)

3. Obtain five test tubes and fill each one half full with the solution from the flask. Set aside one test tube for comparison.

4. To one of the other four test tubes, add fifteen to twenty drops of the potassium thiocyanate solution. Note the change in color. (Record: 2.)

5. To a second test tube, add fifteen to twenty drops of iron (III) chloride solution. Note the change in color. (Record: 3.)

6. To the third test tube, add approximately 1 g of solid potassium chloride, close with a rubber stopper, and shake it well. Note the change in color. (Record: 4.)

7. Using a test tube holder, move the fourth test tube back and forth over a low Bunsen burner flame until you notice a change in color. (Record: 5.)

Remind the students to use distilled water for this procedure.

Data

1. Color of original solution   cherry red

2. Color when potassium thiocyanate was added   deep red

3. Color when iron (III) chloride was added   deep red

4. Color when potassium chloride was added   pale yellow

5. Color when solution was heated   pale yellow

Analysis

1. What substance caused the color of the original solution (Step 2)?

   $Fe(SCN)_3$

2. In which direction did the equilibrium shift when the potassium thiocyanate solution was added to test tube 1? Tell what happened to the concentrations of $Fe(SCN)_3$, KCl, and $FeCl_3$.

   Forward, or to the right; the concentrations of $Fe(SCN)_3$ and KCl increased, and the concentration of $FeCl_3$ decreased.

3. In which direction did the equilibrium shift when iron (III) chloride solution was added to test tube 2? Tell what happened to the concentrations of $Fe(SCN)_3$, KCl, and KSCN.

   Forward, or to the right; the concentrations of $Fe(SCN)_3$ and KCl increased, and the concentration of KSCN decreased.

4. In which direction did the equilibrium shift when potassium chloride was added? Tell what happened to the concentrations of $Fe(SCN)_3$, $FeCl_3$, and KSCN.

   Reverse, or to the left; the concentration of $Fe(SCN)_3$ decreased, and the concentrations of $FeCl_3$ and KSCN increased.

5. In which direction did the equilibrium shift when test tube 4 was heated? Tell what happened to the concentrations of KCl, $Fe(SCN)_3$, $FeCl_3$, and KSCN.

   Reverse, or to the left; the concentrations of $Fe(SCN)_3$ and KCl decreased, and the concentrations of $FeCl_3$ and KSCN increased.

6. As the equation is written in the Concepts section, in the forward direction, is heat a reactant or a product?

   a product

7. Is the forward reaction endothermic or exothermic?

   exothermic

16A Acid-Base Indicators: pH of Household Items and Hydrolysis of Salts

Prelab

Concepts

As you learned in Section 16A of your text, acids may be defined as substances that produce hydronium ions (H_3O^+) in an aqueous solution. Acids that are classified as **strong acids** ionize completely and produce *many* H_3O^+ ions, whereas acids that are classified as **weak acids** ionize to a lesser extent and produce *few* H_3O^+ ions. Since weak acids ionize only slightly, a reversible ionization reaction results, shown in the equation below, where HA represents the weak acid and A^- represents the conjugate base of the weak acid.

$$HA + H_2O \underset{\text{Reverse Reaction}}{\overset{\text{Forward Reaction}}{\rightleftharpoons}} H_3O^+ + A^-$$

The stronger the acid, the more the equilibrium lies toward the right (i.e., the reaction goes more to completion); the weaker the acid, the more the equilibrium lies to the left. Hence, you would expect a strong acid to produce more H_3O^+ ions than a weak acid, even if the same concentration of acid is dissolved in water.

In most cases, the concentration of H_3O^+ present in a solution is quite small and results in a number that is cumbersome, even when it is written in scientific notation. An easier form to use that denotes the acidity of a solution is **pH**, defined as the negative logarithm of the $[H_3O^+]$; remember that a logarithm is an exponent.

$$pH = -\log [H_3O^+]$$

Note that since a pH value is actually an exponent, each unit change in its value represents a ten-fold change in the H_3O^+ molar concentration. For example, a solution with a pH of 3 is ten times more acidic than one with a pH of 4.

In Section 16C of your text, you learned that salts result from neutralization reactions. These salts can be neutral, acidic, or basic, depending on the type of anion and cation composing them. If a cation (HB^+) or an acidic anion reacts with water (hydrolyzes), the general reactions are these.

$$HB^+ + H_2O \rightleftharpoons H_3O^+ + B$$
$$HA^- + H_2O \rightleftharpoons H_3O^+ + A^{2-}$$

As a result, the solution will be acidic because there are more H_3O^+ ions formed. If, however, an anion hydrolyzes, the solution will be basic because OH^- ions are formed, as shown:

$$A^- + H_2O \rightleftharpoons OH^- + HA.$$

In this lab, you will use one or more methods of pH testing to classify certain salts into one of these categories, determined by whether or not they undergo hydrolysis in water.

Acid-base indicators are generally weak organic acids or bases that exist in equilibrium, not only between the conjugate acid-base pair, but also between the two colors that they exhibit. The following equation shows this equilibrium.

$$\underset{\text{Color 1}}{HIn} + H_2O \rightleftharpoons H_3O^+ + \underset{\text{Color 2}}{In^-}$$

Goals

✓ Prepare an acid-base indicator from red cabbage.

✓ Estimate the acidity or basicity of common household items using red cabbage juice and litmus paper.

✓ Explore the hydrolysis of salts in an aqueous solution.

✓ *(Optional)* Determine the pH of several solutions using pH paper or a pH meter, or both.

Materials

acetic acid ($HC_2H_3O_2$), 1 *M*

beakers, 150 mL, 2

Bunsen burner

glass stirring rod

hydrochloric acid (HCl), 0.1 *M*

iron ring

litmus papers, blue and red

matches

pH meter *(optional)*

pH paper, wide range, pH 0–13 *(optional)*

potassium hydrogen phthalate ($KHC_8H_4O_4$, or KHP)

red cabbage

ring stand

sodium carbonate (Na_2CO_3)

sodium chloride (NaCl)

sodium hydrogen carbonate (bicarbonate) ($NaHCO_3$)

sodium hydroxide (NaOH), 0.1 *M*

test tube rack

test tubes, small, 8

transfer pipet

watch glasses, 2

wire gauze

Remind the students that $[H_3O^+]$ is the molar concentration of H_3O^+.

Other plants that contain color-changing pigments are listed in Figure 16-18 in the text.

According to Le Châtelier's principle, the more the concentration of H_3O^+ is increased, the more the equilibrium will shift toward the left; the more the concentration of H_3O^+ is decreased, the more the equilibrium will shift toward the right. The degree of acidity that is necessary to cause this shift will depend on the specific indicator and its K_a value. In any case, color 1 will predominate in solutions that are more acidic than the indicator's K_a, and color 2 will predominate in solutions that are more basic. The pH region over which both colors are present in significant amounts will exhibit a color that is a mixture of them both. Of course, if there is more than one indicator present in a test solution, a greater range of colors is possible.

Certain plants have pigments that belong to a class of molecules known as *anthocyanins*, which are different colors in solutions of different acidity—that is, they can serve as acid-base indicators. In this lab, you will extract the pigments from red cabbage leaves and use the resulting solution to determine the acidity or basicity of several common household items. You will compare the color of each solution to the description in the following table to determine its relative acidity/basicity.

16A-1 **Colors of Solutions**	
Color of solution	**Relative acidity/basicity**
bright red	strong acid
medium red	medium acid
reddish purple	weak acid
purple	near neutral
blue green	weak base
green	medium base
yellow	strong base

Litmus is another colored material that comes from a natural source—certain species of lichens. It is light red in solutions that have a pH less than 5 and it is blue (purplish) in solutions whose pH is greater than 8. Its most common use is in the form of litmus paper—paper strips that have been treated with litmus. Generally, both blue and red litmus papers are used to determine the pH range of a solution. If the pH is between 5 and 8, neither will change color—that is, blue paper remains blue and red remains red; the solution is "neutral."

A more accurate value for the pH of a solution can be obtained by using pH paper, which contains a mixture of indicators. It changes to a specific color that depends on the pH. By comparing the color to a chart, you can get a good estimate of the pH, usually within one pH unit of the actual value. Still more accurate measurements of pH can be obtained by using a pH meter—an electronic device that measures the concentration of H_3O^+. In an optional section of this lab, your teacher may have you determine the pHs of the same solutions using either a pH meter or pH paper, or both.

A "student-proof," solid-state pH electrode is now available from some suppliers and is recommended.

Checkup

1. How would you expect the pH of 0.1 *M* hydrochloric acid to compare with the pH of 0.1 *M* acetic acid? Explain.

   It would be a smaller value (more acidic); HCl is a much stronger acid than acetic acid, resulting in a more acidic solution (more

H_3O^+) and a smaller pH value.

2. What is the pH of a 0.01 M solution of HNO_3, which is a strong
   acid? __pH = 2.0__

3. What is the purpose for boiling the distilled water that you use to
   make up the salt solutions?

   to expel any carbon dioxide that has dissolved in it from the

   atmosphere

4. What color would you expect red cabbage extract to be in a solution of 1 M sulfuric acid? __bright red__

5. Would you expect litmus to appear red, blue, or something in between when it is placed in pure water?

   Pure water is neutral (pH 7) and causes no color change in either

   red or blue litmus paper.

Procedure

1. Prepare the red cabbage extract and boiled distilled water.

   a. Obtain a red cabbage leaf; cut or tear it into small pieces and
      layer them in a 150 mL beaker to a depth of about one inch.

   b. Add just enough distilled water to cover the cabbage and heat
      it to boiling on your ring stand, using your Bunsen burner. Boil
      gently for 2–3 minutes. Remove the beaker from the ring stand
      to cool.

   c. Add about 50 mL of distilled water to another 150 mL beaker
      and allow it to boil for several minutes to expel any dissolved at-
      mospheric carbon dioxide. Cover the beaker with a watch glass
      and allow to cool.

2. Test the acidity/basicity of several known solutions.

   a. Clean four small test tubes and rinse them with distilled water;
      allow them to drain. Label them with the following designations:
      0.1 M HCl, 0.1 M $HC_2H_3O_2$, 0.1 M NaOH, and boiled distilled
      water.

   b. Lay two strips of blue and two strips of red litmus paper on a
      clean watch glass. Pour 2 mL (about 1 in.) of each solution (or
      water) into its labeled tube. Dip a clean stirring rod into the first
      test tube in order to get a droplet of liquid on the end of the rod
      and transfer it to one end of a strip of blue litmus paper. Repeat
      this procedure with red litmus paper. Note the color of each strip
      where it is wet. (Record: 1a–b.) Rinse and dry the stirring rod
      and repeat this procedure for each of the liquids.

   c. Using a clean transfer pipet, add 5 drops of red cabbage extract
      to each of the 4 test tubes from Step 2b; mix by swirling the tube
      and note the color of each mixture. (Record: 3.) You will ob-
      serve several of the colors for red cabbage over a wide pH range.

Dissolved CO_2 forms some H_3O^+ in the ionization of the H_2CO_3 that forms when the
H_2O and the CO_2 react.

A more concentrated red cabbage extract,
which results in better colors, is obtained
if the cabbage leaves are cut into small
pieces prior to boiling them.

Depending on their technique, students may be able to detect a difference in the color of red cabbage extract when comparing hydrochloric acid and acetic acid.

(Could you use red cabbage extract to distinguish between hydrochloric acid and acetic acid?)

d. Fill in the table with your conclusions for the relative acidity/basicity of each of the liquids, based on your observations with litmus and red cabbage extract and the information in Table 16A-1. (Record: 2, 4.)

3. Test the acidity/basicity of several household chemicals.

a. Your teacher will tell you which chemicals you will be testing and may ask you to provide items to test. If the solutions are not already made up for you, prepare them as follows. If the chemical is solid, use about 0.1 g—a volume about equal to a few grains of rice—and dissolve it in about 2 mL of your freshly boiled, cooled, distilled water. If it is a viscous ("syrupy") liquid (e.g., shampoo), mix about 0.5 mL of it with about 1.5 mL freshly boiled distilled water. If it is already a solution, test about 2 mL of it directly with the specified indicator. Suggested chemicals include the following: solid drain cleaner, vinegar, lemon juice, milk of magnesia, household ammonia, baking soda, boric acid eyewash, soap, detergent, shampoo, aspirin (crushed), dishwasher powder, and lemon-lime soft drink.

b. Follow the procedures for testing each chemical with litmus paper, as given in Step 2b. Note the color of the paper for each. (Record: 5a–b.) Determine whether each solution is acidic, basic, or neutral using litmus paper. (Record: 6.)

c. Test each 2 mL portion of solution from Step 3a with red cabbage indicator, using the procedure given in Step 2c. Note the color of each. (Record: 7.) Determine the relative acidity/basicity of each. (Record: 8.)

d. *(Optional)* If assigned to do so, test each solution with pH paper, using strips that are about 1 cm long. Place them on a watch glass and transfer a droplet of each solution being tested to a separate strip, using a clean stirring rod. Be sure to compare the color of the pH paper to the color chart *while the paper is still wet*. Determine the best color match to find the pH. (Record: 9.) *Rinse your stirring rod between each different solution.*

4. Examine the hydrolysis of salts using indicators (and a pH meter).

a. Dissolve about 0.1 g of each salt to be tested in 2 mL of freshly boiled, cooled, distilled water, as you did in Step 3a. Some suggested salts include sodium chloride ($NaCl$), sodium hydrogen carbonate (bicarbonate) ($NaHCO_3$), potassium hydrogen phthalate ($KHC_8H_4O_4$, or KHP), and sodium carbonate (Na_2CO_3). Your teacher may assign others to you, in addition to or in place of these. Label your tubes appropriately.

b. Add 5 drops of the red cabbage indicator to each tube and note the color of each. (Record: 10.) Determine the relative acidity/basicity of each. (Record: 11.)

c. *(Optional)* Using short strips of pH paper on your watch glass, determine the pH of each salt solution as you did in Step 3c. (Record: 12.)

d. *(Optional)* If you are assigned to find the pH of these salt solutions using a pH meter, your teacher will instruct you in its proper use. *Be very careful with this instrument—it is fairly expensive!* Be sure to rinse the electrode with distilled water after each solution tested. To measure the pH with a pH meter, you will need about 25 mL of each solution in small beakers. (If the electrode is slender enough, you may be able to insert it into the test tubes from Step 4a.) Wait until the pH has stabilized before you record the pH. (Record: 13.)

Data

Solutions Tested				
Name of solution:	0.1 *M* HCl	0.1 *M* HC$_2$H$_3$O$_2$	Boiled distilled H$_2$O	0.1 *M* NaOH
1a. Blue litmus	red	red	no change	blue
1b. Red litmus	red	red	no change	blue
2. Acidic, basic, or neutral	acidic	acidic	neutral	basic
3. Red cabbage extract	bright red (dark pink)	medium red (light pink)	purple	yellow-green
4. Relative acidity/basicity	strong acid	medium acid	near neutral	strong base
Household Chemicals Tested				
Name of chemical:				
5a. Blue litmus				
5b. Red litmus				
6. Acidic, basic, or neutral				
7. Red cabbage extract				
8. Relative acidity/basicity				
9. pH, using pH paper *(optional)*				
Salts Tested				
Name of salt:	NaCl	NaHCO$_3$	KHC$_8$H$_4$O$_4$ (KHP)	Na$_2$CO$_3$
10. Red cabbage extract	purple	blue-green	reddish-purple	green
11. Relative acidity/basicity	near neutral	weak base	weak acid	medium base
12. pH, using pH paper *(optional)*	5-6	8-9	4 (approx.)	10-11
13. pH, using pH meter *(optional)*				

The household items that are tested should be recorded in the top row of the Household Chemicals Tested table.

Analysis

1. Based on your findings from this lab, could you differentiate between equal concentrations of hydrochloric acid and acetic acid, using red cabbage extract as an indicator? Explain.

   Yes, hydrochloric acid was more acidic, indicated by the bright red color, whereas acetic acid was not so

   acidic, indicated by the medium red color. These findings resulted from the fact that hydrochloric acid is a

2. Which indicator is a better choice to give you more information concerning a substance's pH—litmus or red cabbage extract? Explain.

    Red cabbage extract. It changes to more than two colors, allowing a better estimate of the relative acidity of

    a substance.

3. Write equations to represent the hydrolysis reactions for those salts where hydrolysis occurred. (In your equation, use only the ions that actually reacted.)

    NaCl—no hydrolysis

    $HCO_3^- + H_2O \rightarrow OH^- + H_2CO_3$

    $HC_8H_4O_4^- + H_2O \rightarrow H_3O^+ + C_8H_4O_4^{2-}$

    $CO_3^{2-} + H_2O \rightarrow HCO_3^- + OH^-$

4. *(Optional)* How well did pH values obtained from pH paper correlate with those obtained from a pH meter?

    Answers will vary, but there should be a good correlation between the pH paper and the pH meter, even

    though the pH meter is more reliable and accurate.

16A Acid-Base Indicators (alternate)

Prelab

Concepts

One definition of acids is that they are compounds that separate (ionize) into H_3O^+ ions and negative ions in water solutions. Acids ionize to varying degrees. Some ionize completely, but most of them ionize to a lesser extent. Acids that ionize completely are called **strong acids**, and acids that ionize only slightly are called **weak acids**.

Since weak acids ionize only slightly, a reversible ionization reaction results. The following reaction demonstrates this reversibility with arrows, one indicating the forward reaction and one indicating the reverse reaction. Let HA represent the weak acid. (A^- represents any anion.)

$$HA \quad + H_2O \quad \underset{\text{Reverse Reaction}}{\overset{\text{Forward Reaction}}{\rightleftharpoons}} \quad H_3O^+ \quad + A^-$$

$$\text{weak acid} + \text{water} \quad \underset{\text{Reverse Reaction}}{\overset{\text{Forward Reaction}}{\rightleftharpoons}} \quad \text{hydronium ion} + \text{anion}$$

At equilibrium, the rates of the forward and reverse reactions are equal. Therefore, the molar concentrations of HA, H_3O^+, and A^- ions can be described by an ionization constant according to the following equation:

$$K_a = \frac{[H_3O^+][A^-]}{[HA]}.$$

Since this equation is used for calculating the ionization constant, K_a, of a *weak* acid, you can make two simplifying assumptions. First, since most of the molecules are *un-ionized*, you can assume that the concentration of the weak acid [HA] approximates the molarity (*M*) of that weak acid. Therefore, you can substitute the molarity of the weak acid for its concentration. Second, since each HA molecule ionizes to form one A^- and one H_3O^+, you can assume that the value of the hydronium ion concentration, $[H_3O^+]$, equals the value of the anion concentration, $[A^-]$. Therefore, if you know the value for the hydronium ion concentration, you also know the value for the anion concentration.

Calculating the ionization constant for a weak acid seems straightforward until you try to find the value for $[H_3O^+]$. How do you find it? You can measure the $[H_3O^+]$ of a solution by comparing the solution to standards of known concentrations.

In this experiment you will make three sets of standards. Each set will cover a range of five concentrations and will contain an acid-base indicator. **Acid-base indicators** are weak organic acids or bases whose molecules appear as one color and whose ions appear as another color—the color of the acid and the color of the conjugate base, respectively—as shown in this equation.

$$\underset{\text{Color 1}}{HIn} \rightleftharpoons H^+ + \underset{\text{Color 2}}{In^-}$$

In solutions that are more acidic than the indicator, the equilibrium lies toward the left and color 1 is seen. If the solution is more basic (less acidic) than the indicator, the equilibrium lies toward the right and color 2 is seen. How acidic or basic the solution must be to favor one color over

Goals

✓ Prepare a set of indicator standards.
✓ Estimate the $[H_3O^+]$ of an acetic acid ($HC_2H_3O_2$) solution.
✓ Find the acid-ionization constant, K_a, of an unknown weak acid.

Materials

acetic acid ($HC_2H_3O_2$), 0.1 *M*
graduated cylinders, 10 mL and 100 mL
hydrochloric acid (HCl), 0.1 *M*
methyl orange solution
methyl red solution
test tube racks, 2
test tubes, 21
thymol blue solution
transfer pipet
unknown weak acid, 1 *M*

Materials

You can use any weak acid, such as 1.0 *M* acetic acid, as the weak acid.

This is the Arrhenius definition.

The ionization constant is just a special case of the equilibrium constant.

Remind the students that the expression [HA] means the concentration of HA in moles per liter.

Because the acid has ionized slightly, the molarity cannot exactly equal the concentration of the weak acid.

the other depends on the specific indicator; each has its own specific pH range over which its color will change. Using several indicators allows you to match a solution of unknown concentration to a standard. Although the color of your solution may not match a standard exactly, the estimated $[H_3O^+]$ will be fairly close.

Often the $[H_3O^+]$ of a solution is a cumbersome number even when it is written in scientific notation. To avoid writing these awkward numbers, scientists developed the pH scale. The pH scale is just a simplified method of expressing the $[H_3O^+]$ of a solution. To calculate the pH of a solution from its $[H_3O^+]$, take the negative logarithm of the $[H_3O^+]$. Remember that a logarithm (log) is an exponent.

$$pH = -\log [H_3O^+]$$

For example, consider a solution in which the $[H_3O^+]$ is 1.0×10^{-7} mol/L. The log of this concentration is −7.00. The −7 came from the power of 10, and the .00 came from the fact that $10^0 = 1$ (log 1 = 0). Since the negative of −7.00 is 7.00, the pH of this concentration is 7.00. And since the exponent must be exact, the integer part of the pH is not included in significant digits considerations. That is, there are as many *decimal places* in the pH as there are significant digits in the coefficient of the concentration written in scientific notation.

Checkup

1. What classifies an acid as a strong acid?

   It completely ionizes in water solutions.

2. How will you find the $[H_3O^+]$ of the $HC_2H_3O_2$ solution and of the unknown weak acid?

   by testing the solutions with indicators to estimate the pH and

   then calculating the $[H_3O^+]$ from the pH equation

3. How would you expect the pH of 0.1 *M* $HC_2H_3O_2$ (a weak acid) to compare with the pH of 0.1 *M* HCl? Explain.

   The pH will be higher—less acidic—because $HC_2H_3O_2$ ionizes

   less completely than HCl, producing fewer H_3O^+ ions and hence

   a larger pH.

4. In general, what chemical composition does an acid-base indicator have? What is its purpose?

   An acid-base indicator is a weak organic acid or base whose

   molecules appear as one color and whose ions appear as

   another color. Since an indicator changes color over a specific

   pH range, it can be used to estimate the pH of a solution.

5. How many different sets of indicators will you make? How many samples will each set contain?

   three; five

The pH of a solution is found with either a pH meter or an indicator.

Procedure

1. Prepare the indicator standards.

   a. Obtain two test tube racks and twenty-one test tubes.

   b. Label five test tubes 1A–1E, five test tubes 2A–2E, and five test tubes 3A–3E.

   c. Add about 15 mL of 0.1 M (1×10^{-1} M) HCl solution to a 100 mL graduated cylinder.

   d. Using your 10 mL graduated cylinder, measure 3 mL portions of the HCl into test tubes 1A, 2A, and 3A.

   e. You should have 6 mL of 0.1 M HCl remaining in the 100 mL graduated cylinder. Add water up to the 60 mL mark and mix well. This dilutes the acid to 0.01 M (1×10^{-2} M) HCl.

   f. Using your cleaned and rinsed 10 mL graduated cylinder, pour 3 mL portions of the 0.01 M HCl into test tubes 1B, 2B, and 3B.

   g. Repeat Steps 1e–f to make these dilutions for the following test tubes:

   0.001 M (1×10^{-3} M) HCl in test tubes 1C, 2C, and 3C;

   0.0001 M (1×10^{-4} M) HCl in test tubes 1D, 2D, and 3D;

   0.00001 M (1×10^{-5} M) HCl in test tubes 1E, 2E, and 3E.

   h. To each solution in test tubes 1A, 1B, 1C, 1D, and 1E, add three drops of thymol blue solution. Shake the solutions well and record the color of each. (Record: 1–5.)

   i. To each solution in test tubes 2A, 2B, 2C, 2D, and 2E, add three drops of methyl orange solution. Shake the solutions well and record the color of each. (Record: 1–5.)

   j. To each solution in test tubes 3A, 3B, 3C, 3D, and 3E, add three drops of methyl red solution. Shake the solutions well and record the color of each. (Record: 1–5.)

2. Determine the $[H_3O^+]$ of a 0.1 M $HC_2H_3O_2$ solution by comparing it to the indicator standards.

   a. Measure 3 mL portions of a 0.1 M $HC_2H_3O_2$ solution into three test tubes.

   b. Add three drops of thymol blue solution to the first test tube of $HC_2H_3O_2$, three drops of methyl orange solution to the second, and three drops of methyl red solution to the third.

   c. Determine the $[H_3O^+]$ in the $HC_2H_3O_2$ solution by comparing the color of the thymol blue test to the group 1 standards from Step 1. If you do not get a perfect match, estimate the hydronium ion concentration. (Record: 6.)

   d. Compare the methyl orange test to group 2 standards from Procedure 1. (Record: 7.)

   e. Compare the methyl red test to group 3 standards from Procedure 1. (Record: 8.)

3. Determine the $[H_3O^+]$ of a 1 M unknown weak acid by comparing it to the indicator standards. Repeat Steps 2a–e for three 3 mL samples of a 1 M unknown weak acid. (Record: 9–11.)

This is calculated according to the formula $M_iV_i = M_fV_f$, where M_i is 0.1, V_i is 6 mL, and V_f is 60 mL.

Data

| | | | | Indicator Color | |
Test tubes	$[H_3O^+]$	pH	Thymol blue	Methyl orange	Methyl red
1. Group A	1.0×10^{-1}				
2. Group B	1.0×10^{-2}				
3. Group C	1.0×10^{-3}				
4. Group D	1.0×10^{-4}				
5. Group E	1.0×10^{-5}				

6. The $[H_3O^+]$ of the $HC_2H_3O_2$ solution from the thymol blue test _____

7. The $[H_3O^+]$ of the $HC_2H_3O_2$ solution from the methyl orange test _____

8. The $[H_3O^+]$ of the $HC_2H_3O_2$ solution from the methyl red test _____

9. The $[H_3O^+]$ of the unknown weak acid from the thymol blue test _____

10. The $[H_3O^+]$ of the unknown weak acid from the methyl orange test _____

11. The $[H_3O^+]$ of the unknown weak acid from the methyl red test _____

Analysis

1. The standard solutions.
   a. Using the equation $pH = -\log [H_3O^+]$, calculate the pH of the standard solutions prepared in Step 1. Enter the values on the data table. (Record: 1–5.)
   b. What effect does a dilution by a factor of 10 (for example, from 1×10^{-7} to 1×10^{-8}) have on the pH of an HCl solution? __It raises it by 1 pH unit (for example, from 7 to 8).__
   c. Estimate the pH range over which each of the indicators changes color.
      thymol blue—1.2–2.8; methyl orange—3.2–4.4; methyl red—4.2–6.2
      (Student values will not be this precise.)

2. What was the approximate pH of the 0.1 M $HC_2H_3O_2$ solution? Explain your answer.
   The pH is about 3. Its colors best matched the Group C set of standards.

3. Calculations for the 1 M weak acid.
   a. What was the $[H_3O^+]$ in the sample of 1 M weak acid? (*Hint*: Check your data.)
      Answer depends on the acid used.
   b. Let HA represent the formula of the weak acid. What was the $[A^-]$? (*Hint*: Review the two assumptions.)
      Answer depends on the acid used, but it should be the same as 3a.
   c. What was the $[HA]$? (*Hint*: Review the two assumptions.) __$[HA] = 1 M$__
   d. Substituting values from Analysis sections 3a–c into the expression of K_a for the acid, calculate the value of K_a.
      Answer depends on the acid used.

Since a weak acid ionizes only slightly, you can expect the K_a to be small. The K_a for acetic acid is 1.8×10^{-5}.

16B Acid-Base Titrations: Acetic Acid in Vinegar

Prelab

Concepts

You can determine the concentration of one unknown solution by measuring the volume of a second known solution that reacts completely with it. When you do this, you are performing a volumetric analysis. As the name implies, a volumetric analysis depends on measuring a volume accurately. Certain types of glassware—burets, pipets, and volumetric flasks—allow you to make these accurate measurements.

One of the most common volumetric techniques is called a **titration**. This technique uses a buret to measure the volume of a substance that reacts completely with a measured amount of another substance. There are two things you must know in order to use this technique: (1) what a buret is and (2) how to tell when a reaction is complete. First, a buret is a long, glass cylinder with a valve at one end and volume markings along its side. The valve allows small, precise amounts of liquid to be released from the buret. The graduations marked along the cylinder allow the volume of released liquid to be measured. Second, the formation of a precipitate often signals the completion of a soluble-salt titration, and an indicator signals the completion (end point) of an acid-base or an oxidation-reduction titration.

In this experiment, you will perform the most common type of titration: an acid-base titration. In Part A, you will determine the molar concentration of the NaOH solution by titrating it with a primary standard using phenolphthalein as the indicator. A *primary standard* is a chemical substance that is easy to work with and of such purity that it can be used as a reference. Your primary standard is the organic acid salt, potassium hydrogen phthalate ($KHC_8H_4O_4$, or KHP). Using the grams of KHP that you measured into the solution and the volume of NaOH solution needed to react with all of it, you can calculate the molarity of the NaOH solution according to the following steps:

1. Divide the grams of KHP by the molar mass (204 g/mol) to get the moles of KHP that reacted.

2. Assume that this number of moles of KHP equals the number of moles of NaOH reacted because the ions in KHP and NaOH react in a 1:1 ratio.

3. Divide the number of moles of NaOH reacted by the volume of solution containing it to get moles per liter—the molarity of NaOH.

$$\frac{\text{moles NaOH}}{\text{liters solution}} = \text{molarity}$$

In Part B, you will use your standardized solution of NaOH and the indicator phenolphthalein to determine the molarity of acid in a sample of commercial vinegar. Using the molarity and volume of the NaOH and the volume of the vinegar, you can calculate the molarity of the acetic acid in vinegar according to the following formula, which is valid only because acetic acid and NaOH react in a 1:1 mole ratio.

$$M_{\text{vinegar}} \times V_{\text{vinegar}} = M_{\text{NaOH}} \times V_{\text{NaOH}}$$

Goals

✓ Use the technique of titration.

✓ Standardize a solution of sodium hydroxide, using potassium hydrogen phthalate as the primary standard.

✓ Calculate the molarity of commercial vinegar, using the standardized sodium hydroxide solution.

✓ Calculate the percent by mass of acetic acid contained in vinegar.

✓ *(Optional)* Compare the amounts of acetic acid contained in two brands of vinegar.

Materials

balance

beakers, 150 mL, 2

buret clamp

burets, 2

commercial vinegar

Erlenmeyer flask, 250 mL

eyedropper

filtering funnel

marker, black

phenolphthalein solution

potassium hydrogen phthalate ($KHC_8H_4O_4$, or KHP)

ring stand

sodium hydroxide (NaOH) solution

wash bottle

Materials

In place of burets, 5 mL pipets may be used to measure out the vinegar in Parts B and C.

Use approximately 0.1 *M* NaOH.

Provide the phenolphthalein in plastic dropper bottles for easy dispensing. One or two for every 10 groups is sufficient.

Pronunciation key for phenolphthalein: FEE nole THAY leen.

The *end point* is the point at which the indicator changes color because the two reagents are chemically or stoichiometrically equivalent—they have reacted according to a balanced chemical equation.

From this molarity of vinegar, you will then be able to calculate the percent by mass of acetic acid in commercial vinegar. Using the molarity of acetic acid in vinegar and the molar mass of acetic acid ($HC_2H_3O_2$, 60.0 g/mol), you can determine the mass of acetic acid in a measured volume of vinegar. Assuming the density of vinegar to be 1.01 g/mL, you can then find the mass of the vinegar sample and thus the percent by mass. (See text, Section 12B.) The calculation is summarized as follows (HOAc represents acetic acid):

$$\frac{x \text{ mol } \cancel{HOAc}}{\cancel{L} \text{ vinegar}} \left| \frac{60.0 \text{ g HOAc}}{1 \text{ mol } \cancel{HOAc}} \right| \frac{1 \cancel{L}}{1000 \text{ mL}} \left| \frac{1 \cancel{mL} \text{ vinegar}}{1.01 \text{ g vinegar}} \right| \frac{100\%}{} = \% \text{ HOAc in vinegar by mass.}$$

In an optional section, your teacher may have you compare several different brands of vinegar to see if less expensive brands differ significantly from more expensive ones in terms of their acetic acid content.

Checkup

1. What is the main purpose of Part A?

   to standardize the NaOH solution—that is, to find its concentration by using the primary standard, KHP

2. Once you have weighed out the KHP or measured out the vinegar, why is it *not* important to measure the volume of water you add?

   You are titrating the KHP or the vinegar, not the water, and you already know how much of it is present. Adding more or less water will not change how much of the measured reacting substance is present.

3. What is molarity?

   concentration units; molarity—moles of solute per liter of solution

4. Define *titration*.

   a volumetric technique using a buret to measure the volume of one substance that is necessary to react completely with a known amount of another substance

5. What three types of reactions can you utilize in titrations?

   a soluble-salt reaction, an acid-base reaction, and an oxidation-reduction reaction

Procedure

Part A: Standardizing the NaOH Solution

1. Add about 100 mL of NaOH solution to a clean, dry 150 mL beaker.

2. Thoroughly clean a buret by rinsing it with water several times. When the buret is clean, the water will drain out evenly without leaving water spots on the inside walls. Rinse the buret twice with a few milliliters of the NaOH solution. Be sure to rinse the tip as well, allowing solution to drain out of the buret. Then place the buret in a clamp. (See Figure 16B-1.)

3. Close the stopcock and, with the aid of a funnel, carefully fill the buret with NaOH solution. Open the stopcock and drain out some of the solution until the tip of the buret is filled. Add NaOH solution to the buret, if necessary, until the level of the liquid is near but not above 0 mL. Record the volume to 0.01 mL. (Record: Part A1.) Remember to read *down* a buret (i.e., the volume at the top marking is 0 mL and at the bottom marking is 50 mL). You can see the meniscus more easily if you hold a "buret card" behind the buret—a 3 × 5 in. white card with a thick black marker line on it. If you place the card so that the black mark is just below the meniscus, it will be more visible.

4. Determine the mass of your 250 mL Erlenmeyer flask. (It need not be dry inside.) (Record: Part A2.) Add 0.5–0.6 g of potassium hydrogen phthalate (KHP) to the flask on the scale. (Record: Part A3.)

5. Add about 30 mL of distilled water to the flask (it need not be measured accurately), and swirl the flask until all the solid dissolves. Wash any crystals that cling to the wall of the flask down into the solution with a few milliliters of water from a wash bottle.

6. Add two drops of phenolphthalein indicator to the KHP solution in the flask.

7. Place the flask on a piece of white paper under the buret. Lower the buret until the tip extends into the flask.

8. Titrate the KHP solution by adding a few milliliters of NaOH solution from the buret as you swirl the flask to mix the solutions. (See Figure 16B-2.) Control the stopcock with one hand while you swirl the flask with the other hand. Continue to titrate by adding the NaOH solution slowly until the light pink color lingers before disappearing; then add the NaOH by drops. Stop titrating when the light pink color remains for at least thirty seconds; you have reached the *end point*. If the pink color fades, add one more drop at a time until there is a change from colorless to a permanent pink. Read the volume in the buret to the nearest 0.01 mL. (Record: Part A4.)

9. Refill the buret nearly to the 0 mL mark with NaOH solution and record that volume. (Record: Part A1.) Make a new sample of KHP solution as you did in Steps 4–7. To verify your results, repeat the titration in Part A, Step 8. (Record: Part A2–4.)

10. Refill the buret with NaOH solution for Part B.

16B-1   Acid-base titration

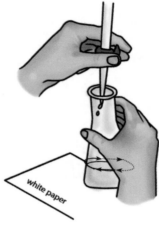

16B-2   Proper titration technique

white paper

If you wish to compare vinegar brands, you may wish to standardize the base yourself and provide its concentration. Otherwise, doing all three parts during one lab period may not be possible. Also, if time is short, you may allow students to do only one vinegar titration. (Of course, this would eliminate any "averages" for vinegar in the Analysis section.)

You will need to plan on demonstrating to the class the setup and titration technique, using good methods yourself.

Unless your water is quite hard or greater accuracy is desired, the students do not need to use distilled water for this procedure.

Phenolphthalein is colorless in an acid (KHP in this case) and pink or red in a base.

The white paper makes the color change easier to see.

If the students go beyond the end point, they will have to start over by making a new primary standard solution.

To save time and to eliminate the need for each group to have 2 burets, students may obtain their vinegar sample from a single buret, located at a central location where the teacher can monitor its use and refill it. In that case, each group would bring its flask to get 5 mL, as in Part B, Step 4.

Erlenmeyer flasks are used for titrations because the sloped sides allow liquids to be swirled with less likelihood of splashing out of the container.

Remind students to use distilled water for this procedure, if necessary.

The ratios of the volume of NaOH to the volume of vinegar used in the two titrations should agree within 1 to 2 percent.

Part B: Titrating the Vinegar

1. Obtain about 30 mL of vinegar in a clean, dry 150 mL beaker.

2. Thoroughly clean a second buret as you did before, and rinse it out twice with a few milliliters of vinegar, including the tip. Place the buret in the clamp.

3. Fill the buret with vinegar to about the 35 mL mark. Be sure to fill the tip by opening the stopcock for a moment. Read the volume in the buret to the nearest 0.1 mL. (Record: Part B1.)

4. Allow about 5 mL of the vinegar to drain into a clean 250 mL Erlenmeyer flask. (It need not be dry.) Add about 20 mL of distilled water and two drops of phenolphthalein indicator to the vinegar in the flask.

5. Read the volume in the NaOH buret. (Record: Part B2.)

6. Titrate the vinegar in the flask with the NaOH solution from the buret.

7. If you go past the end point, add a few drops of vinegar from the buret and then carefully add NaOH until one drop causes the color to change to pink. Read and record the volumes in the NaOH and vinegar burets. (Record: Part B3–4.)

8. Repeat the titration in Steps 4–7 with a second sample of vinegar. *Be sure to read the volumes in the burets before the titration* (Record: Part B1–2.) *and after the titration!* (Record: Part B3–4.)

9. When you are sure you are finished with your titrations, rinse out your burets, *including the tips*, using several rinses with tap water, followed by a final rinse with distilled water.

Part C: (Optional) Comparison of Brands of Vinegar

1. Empty your buret containing the vinegar into the sink. Obtain about 30 mL of a different brand of vinegar in a clean, dry 150 mL beaker. Rinse the buret that contained the vinegar in Part B twice with several milliliters of the second brand of vinegar. Be sure to rinse out the tip as well. Place the buret in the buret clamp.

2. Repeat Part B, Steps 3–9, and record the volume readings in the appropriate blanks. (Record: Part C1–4.)

Data

Part A: Standardizing the NaOH Solution

	Trial 1	Trial 2
1. Initial volume of NaOH	_____ mL	_____ mL
2. Mass of flask	_____ g	_____ g
3. Mass of flask and $KHC_8H_4O_4$	_____ g	_____ g
4. Final volume of NaOH	_____ mL	_____ mL
5. Volume of NaOH used (4. – 1.)	_____ mL	_____ mL

Part B: Titrating the Vinegar

Brand name _____   Cost per oz _____

	Trial 1	Trial 2
1. Initial volume of vinegar	_____ mL	_____ mL
2. Initial volume of NaOH	_____ mL	_____ mL
3. Final volume of vinegar	_____ mL	_____ mL
4. Final volume of NaOH	_____ mL	_____ mL
5. Volume of NaOH used (4. – 2.)	_____ mL	_____ mL
6. Volume of vinegar titrated (3. – 1.)	_____ mL	_____ mL

Part C: (Optional) Comparison of Brands of Vinegar

Brand name _____   Cost per oz _____

	Trial 1	Trial 2
1. Initial volume of vinegar	_____ mL	_____ mL
2. Initial volume of NaOH	_____ mL	_____ mL
3. Final volume of vinegar	_____ mL	_____ mL
4. Final volume of NaOH	_____ mL	_____ mL
5. Volume of NaOH used (4. – 2.)	_____ mL	_____ mL
6. Volume of vinegar titrated (3. – 1.)	_____ mL	_____ mL

Analysis

Part A: Standardizing the NaOH Solution

	Trial 1	Trial 2
1. Calculate the number of grams of $KHC_8H_4O_4$ used in the standardization of NaOH (Data A3 – A2).	_____ g	_____ g
2. Calculate the number of moles of $KHC_8H_4O_4$ (204 g/mol) used.	_____ mol	_____ mol
3. Calculate the molarity of the NaOH solution for Trial 1 and for Trial 2.	_____ M	_____ M
4. What is the average molarity of the NaOH solution?	_____ M	

Part B: Titrating the Vinegar

	Trial 1	Trial 2
1. Using the molarity and volume of the standardized NaOH, calculate the molarity of the commercial vinegar.	_____ M	_____ M
2. What is the average molarity for the two trials?	_____ M	
3. Using the equation in the Concepts section and the average molarity, calculate the percent acetic acid in commercial vinegar by mass.	_____ %	

Part C: (Optional) Comparison of Brands of Vinegar

	Trial 1	Trial 2
1. Using the molarity and volume of NaOH, calculate the molarity of the second commercial vinegar.	_____ M	_____ M
2. What is the average molarity for the two trials?	_____ M	
3. Calculate the percent acetic acid in this brand of commercial vinegar.	_____ %	

_____
_____
_____
_____
_____
_____
_____
_____
_____

4. Is there a significant difference between the brands of vinegar?

Answers will vary.

5. Is the difference in cost justified? Support your answer.

Answers will vary.

17A Oxidation-Reduction Titration: Comparison of Commercial Bleaches

Prelab

Concepts

Originally, scientists applied the term *oxidation* to the combining of oxygen with other elements, and the term *reduction* to the removing of oxygen from oxides. Today these terms are more general in meaning. **Oxidation** is now defined as a process in which a substance loses electrons (becomes oxidized), and **reduction** is a process in which a substance gains electrons (becomes reduced).

Since the processes of oxidation and reduction must take place in the same reaction, such a reaction is referred to as an **oxidation-reduction (redox) reaction**. You can easily identify redox reactions by checking to see whether there has been a change in oxidation numbers. An increase in the oxidation number indicates oxidation, and a decrease in the oxidation number indicates reduction.

You can determine the concentration of a substance that is easily oxidized by titrating it with an oxidizing agent in much the same way as you titrate an acid with a base. (See Lab 16B.) Although the procedure for titrating these two reactions is the same, the indicators are different. Acid-base indicators change color over a certain pH range because the acid and base in the conjugate pair have different colors. Near the end point, adding more base shifts the equilibrium in favor of the base form and results in its color predominating. However, in some redox titrations, such as this one, the color changes at the end point because the first drop of excess titrant reacts with another molecule to produce a color.

In this lab, you will be using a measured quantity of a solution of sodium hypochlorite (NaOCl)—the oxidizing agent in household chlorine bleaches—to oxidize an iodide ion (I^-) to iodine (I_2) in the presence of acetic acid. The net equation is as follows:

$$2I^- (aq) + OCl^- (aq) + 2HC_2H_3O_2 (aq) \longrightarrow I_2 (aq) + Cl^- (aq) + H_2O (l) + 2C_2H_3O_2^- (aq).$$

Equation 1

The iodine that forms in this reaction will then be titrated with a standard solution of sodium thiosulfate ($Na_2S_2O_3$)—one of known concentration—which will reduce the iodine back to iodide. A starch suspension serves well as an indicator here because it reacts with I_2 to produce a dark blue color, but it is colorless in the presence of the iodide ion (I^-). Thus, the drop of titrant (sodium thiosulfate solution) that reduces the last bit of the iodide will cause the blue color to disappear; this signals the end point. The net ionic equation for this titration is as follows:

$$2S_2O_3^{2-} (aq) + I_2 (aq) \longrightarrow S_4O_6^{2-} (aq) + 2I^- (aq).$$

Equation 2

Since iodine solutions are brown, the end point could also be signaled by a disappearance of the brown color. However, that color change is not nearly as obvious as it is when starch is present and the solution changes from dark blue to colorless.

In this lab, you will also compare different brands of bleach based on the percent by mass of NaOCl they contain per unit volume of bleach

Goals

✓ Review the technique of titration.

✓ Determine the concentration of the oxidizing agent in household bleaches using the technique of titration.

✓ Compare several brands of household bleach to see whether there are significant differences.

Materials

acetic acid, concentrated (glacial)

balance

beaker, 150 mL

buret, 50 mL

buret clamp

chlorine bleach, 2 brands (minimum)

Erlenmeyer flask, 250 mL

filtering funnel

graduated cylinders, 10 mL and 100 mL

potassium iodide (KI)

sodium thiosulfate ($Na_2S_2O_3$) solution, 0.100 *M*

starch suspension, 0.5%

Materials

Rather than using burets or pipets to dispense the bleach, you may wish to have students use an eyedropper to deliver 2 mL of bleach. Calibration of the eyedropper is necessary. Weigh the $Na_2S_2O_3$ accurately; although it is not a primary standard, it is fine for this application.

See Lab 18C for instructions on how to prepare a starch suspension.

(mass/volume percent). You will calculate this amount by using the stoichiometry of the reactions above and the volume of bleach analyzed, according to this dimensional analysis setup.

$$\% \text{ NaOCl} = \dfrac{x \text{ mL } S_2O_3{}^{2-} \left| \dfrac{1 \cancel{L}}{1000 \cancel{mL}} \right| \dfrac{0.100 \cancel{\text{ mol } S_2O_3{}^{2-}}}{\cancel{L}} \left| \dfrac{1 \cancel{\text{ mol } I_2}}{2 \cancel{\text{ mol } S_2O_3{}^{2-}}} \right| \dfrac{1 \cancel{\text{ mol NaOCl}}}{1 \cancel{\text{ mol } I_2}} \left| \dfrac{74.4 \text{ g NaOCl}}{1 \cancel{\text{ mol NaOCl}}} \right. \times 100\%}{2.00 \cancel{\text{ mL}} \text{ bleach}}$$

Equation 3

This equation simplifies to the following equation:

$$\% \text{ NaOCl} = x \text{ mL } S_2O_3{}^{2-} \text{ solution} \times 0.186\%.$$

Once you have determined the percent of NaOCl in each of the bleaches, you will compare them in *cost per mass of NaOCl*—the active component—rather than just the cost per gallon of liquid bleach.

Checkup

1. What distinguishes a redox reaction from other types of reactions?

   A redox reaction is a reaction in which the oxidation number of an element changes.

2. Write out the reaction that occurs during the titration. Circle the reactant that becomes oxidized and underline the reactant that becomes reduced.

   $2S_2O_3{}^{2-} (aq) + I_2 (aq) \rightarrow S_4O_6{}^{2-} (aq) + I^- (aq)$

3. What is the active component—the one that does the bleaching—in liquid chlorine bleach?

   sodium hypochlorite, NaOCl (or hypochlorite ion, OCl⁻)

4. What color change will you observe in the titration that will signal the end point?

   from blue to colorless

5. What is the stoichiometric relationship between the moles of bleaching agent and the moles of iodine actually titrated?

   They are in a 1:1 mole ratio.

6. If the titration of the iodine formed by using 2.00 mL of bleach requires 33.9 mL of 0.100 M $Na_2S_2O_3$ solution to reach the end point, what is the percent by mass of NaOCl in the bleach?

   6.30% NaOCl (mass/volume %)

Procedure

1. Prepare the materials.

   a. Obtain about 80 mL of standard 0.100 M $Na_2S_2O_3$ solution in a clean, *dry* 150 mL beaker.

   b. Rinse the inside walls of your buret twice with approximately 5 mL portions of the $Na_2S_2O_3$ solution; be sure to include the tip. Discard the rinses into the sink.

c. With the aid of a filtering funnel, fill the buret with the $Na_2S_2O_3$ solution to slightly above the 0 mL mark. Drain out a sufficient amount of solution to bring the liquid level down to the zero mark (or slightly below it); be certain to drive all the air from the tip. Making sure that your eye is on the same level as the meniscus, read the initial volume of liquid in the buret to 0.01 mL. (Record: 2.) You may use the buret card from Lab 16B.

d. Obtain approximately 3.5 g of potassium iodide (KI) in a 250 mL Erlenmeyer flask. (The amount need not be weighed accurately.) Add about 50 mL of distilled water and 10 mL of acetic acid and swirl the flask to dissolve the KI.

e. From the buret at the front of the room, obtain a 2.00 mL sample of bleach A in your flask; swirl the flask to mix. It should turn a brownish yellow color, indicating the presence of iodine.

2. Titrate the acidic iodine solution.

a. Immediately titrate the iodine solution with your standard $Na_2S_2O_3$ solution from your buret. You may allow the titrant to enter the iodine-bleach solution fairly rapidly at the beginning; swirl the flask as you add the $Na_2S_2O_3$ solution until the yellowish color is *almost* gone, but *do not go too far!* Then add about 2 mL of the starch suspension to the partially titrated mixture. It should turn dark blue; if it does not, you added too much $Na_2S_2O_3$ solution and will need to start over at Step 1d.

b. Now add the $Na_2S_2O_3$ solution drop by drop as you swirl the flask until the blue color just disappears. Read the final volume in the buret to 0.01 mL. (Record: 1.)

c. Discard the titrated solution down the drain and rinse out the flask with plenty of water, followed by a distilled water rinse.

d. Repeat Steps 1c–2c, using a second 2.00 mL sample of bleach A. (Record: 1–2.)

e. *(Optional)* Your teacher may instruct you to repeat the titration a third time; if so, repeat Steps 1c–2c and record your data. (Record: 1–2.)

f. Repeat Steps 1c–2c for your two (or three) 2.00 mL samples of bleach B, recording the data in the appropriate blanks in the Data section of the lab. (Record: 1–2.)

Data

	Bleach A			Bleach B		
	brand = _____ *cost* = _____			*brand* = _____ *cost* = _____		
	Trial 1	Trial 2	Trial 3 (optional)	Trial 1	Trial 2	Trial 3 (optional)
1. Final volume, mL						
2. Initial volume, mL						
3. Volume $Na_2S_2O_3$ used, mL (2. – 1.)						

It may be useful to have a comparison sample available in a test tube so that they will not need to weigh it out at all.

You may wish to use graduated pipets instead of burets for accurate delivery of bleach.

Starch is not added at the beginning of the titration because the complex compound of I_2 and starch does not quickly dissociate.

Collect the acetic acid wastes in a labeled container and neutralize them with 6 *M* NaOH solution before flushing them down the drain with large volumes of water.

Analysis

	Bleach A	Bleach B
1. Average volume $Na_2S_2O_3$ used	_____ mL	_____ mL
2. Average % NaOCl (g NaOCl per 100 mL bleach)	_____ %	_____ %
3. Cost per gallon of bleach	_____ ¢/gal	_____ ¢/gal
4. Convert your average percent (2.) to a decimal and multiply it by 3785 (the number of mL per gallon) to find the mass of NaOCl per gallon of bleach.	_____ g/gal	_____ g/gal
5. Divide the cost (3.) by the mass of NaOCl (4.) to find the cost per gram of NaOCl.	_____ ¢/g	_____ ¢/g

6. Was the more expensive bleach a better value? Support your answer.

   Answers will vary.

   _____

7. Based on what you observed from this lab, is it possible to pay more for a smaller volume of liquid bleach, and still get a better value? Explain.

   Answers will vary.

   _____

8. If your buret had an air bubble in the tip and it became dislodged during the titration, would the *actual* % NaOCl be larger, smaller, or the same as what you *calculated*?

   The actual would be smaller; the measured volume of titrant would be larger than it should be.

17B Corrosion

Prelab

Concepts

Many redox reactions are found in industrial applications. In fact, electrochemistry, a separate branch of chemistry dealing with the relationship between electricity and chemistry, has developed around redox reactions. Electrochemistry involves either a redox reaction that produces electricity (batteries), or electricity that produces a redox reaction (electroplating). However, electrochemical reactions do not always benefit industry. For example, the electrochemical problem of corrosion (primarily the corrosion of iron) costs industry billions of dollars every year.

Iron corrodes in the presence of water and oxygen. This electrochemical process occurs in several steps as shown in Figure 17B-1. The iron beneath the water droplet gets oxidized to Fe^{2+} ions, establishing an anode. This redox reaction produces electrons and Fe^{2+} ions that migrate to the edge of the water droplet. (Recall that the movement of electrons is electricity.) Here the electrons reduce water and oxygen to form OH^- ions, thus establishing a cathode. The OH^- ions unite with the Fe^{2+} ions at the cathode, producing $Fe(OH)_2$. This compound reacts with oxygen to be oxidized further and produce rust, hydrated iron (III) oxide (Fe_2O_3). The corrosion process is actually more complicated than this, and the form of the product will depend on the availability of water and oxygen.

Goal
✓ Observe factors related to corrosion.

Materials
agar
balance
beaker, 250 mL
copper wire
crucible tongs
glass stirring rod
iron nails, sixpenny (6d), 4
paper towel
phenolphthalein solution, 0.5%
potassium ferricyanide ($K_3Fe[CN]_6$), 0.1 *M*
sandpaper
sodium chloride (NaCl)
test tubes, 4
tin strip (Sn)
zinc strip (Zn)

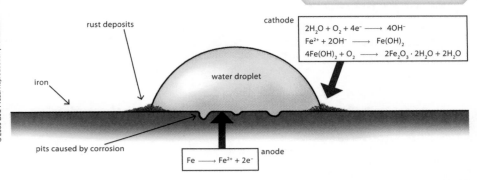

cathode
$$2H_2O + O_2 + 4e^- \longrightarrow 4OH^-$$
$$Fe^{2+} + 2OH^- \longrightarrow Fe(OH)_2$$
$$4Fe(OH)_2 + O_2 \longrightarrow 2Fe_2O_3 \cdot 2H_2O + 2H_2O$$

rust deposits

water droplet

iron

pits caused by corrosion

$$Fe \longrightarrow Fe^{2+} + 2e^-$$ anode

17B-1 Corrosion of iron under a droplet of water

Many facts about corrosion are easily explained in terms of electrochemistry. For example, iron does not corrode in dry air because there is no solution environment in which the ions can move. However, if the solution environment contains dissolved salt particles, then the iron corrodes faster than when it is in the presence of pure water. This is

Materials

Plain gelatin may be used in place of agar, but it requires about an 8%–10% (weight/volume) suspension for room-temperature gelling.

A redox reaction involves the transfer of electrons.

Actually, the compound seems to contain an indefinite amount of water molecules, so it is more accurate to write it as $Fe_2O_3 \cdot nH_2O$.

This occurs in areas near the coast or in the North where salts are spread on the roads to melt ice during winter.

because the salt ions help electrical charges to migrate through the solution. In addition to these examples, electrochemistry can also explain how iron can be protected from corrosion. If the iron is in contact with a more active metal, the more active metal will corrode more easily, thus protecting the iron. This occurs because the more active metal acts as the anode, forcing the iron in contact with it to become the cathode. A less active metal than iron, on the other hand, forces iron to be the anode while it becomes the cathode; corrosion occurs more rapidly. In this exercise, you will explore the effect of other metals on the protection of iron.

Checkup

1. What indicator will you use in this lab to reveal the location of OH⁻ ions? What color will it turn?

   phenolphthalein; pink

2. What indicator will show the location of Fe^{2+} ions? What color will it turn?

   potassium ferricyanide; blue

3. Since there is a transfer of electrons (an electrical current) produced by the chemical reactions of rusting, what kind of reaction is the corrosion reaction?   a redox reaction

4. What half-reaction will take place at the anode? Will this produce corrosion (pits) or rust deposits?

   the oxidation of Fe to Fe^{2+}; corrosion pits

5. Most metals produce oxides that form a protective layer to prevent further corrosion. Give a possible reason why the oxide that iron produces does *not* protect the metal beneath it.

   Since rust flakes off as it forms, it exposes new metal

   underneath.

6. Will iron rust in dry air? Why or why not?

   No. A solution is required for the ions to flow and complete a

   voltaic cell.

Procedure

1. Prepare an agar gel. This gel holds the nails stationary and greatly slows diffusion of the products of corrosion away from the areas where they are produced.

   a. Boil 100 mL of water in a 250 mL beaker.

   b. Add 0.5 g of agar to the water and boil it until it appears that the agar has dissolved. (It is actually a colloidal suspension.)

   c. Stir in 5 g of NaCl.

   d. Add 2 mL phenolphthalein solution and 1 mL 0.1 *M* potassium ferricyanide, stir well, and discontinue heating. The phenolphthalein indicates the cathode reaction (where the rust deposits)

You can extend Question 5 with this information: The aluminum cans now used for beverages are potentially more of a long-range disposal problem than the older tin-plated iron cans. Why? Aluminum cans form an oxide that acts as a protective coating; therefore, they do not corrode as completely as tin-plated iron cans do.

Remind the students to use distilled water for these procedures.

The potassium ferricyanide indicator will turn blue only if iron corrodes.

because it turns pink in the presence of OH⁻ ions. The potassium ferricyanide indicates the anode reaction (where the iron dissolves or pits) because it turns blue in the presence of the Fe^{2+} ions.

2. Clean the nails thoroughly with the sandpaper as necessary, being certain that there is no trace of corrosion remaining. Wipe them with a dry paper towel.

3. Test to see which metals will prevent the corrosion of iron.

   a. Place one nail in a test tube and label it "experimental control."

   b. Wrap a piece of copper wire tightly around the end of a second nail near the head. Extend the excess ends at right angles to the nail. (See Figure 17B-2 in the Data section.) Place the nail in a test tube labeled "copper wire."

   c. Drive the third nail through a zinc strip and the fourth through a piece of tin. Place these in separate tubes and label them appropriately.

   d. Add sufficient indicator gel prepared in Step 1 to submerge each nail completely. Do not disturb the nails until the agar has gelled. If pink and blue areas have not developed by the end of the lab period, store them until the next day. Sketch the white, pink, and blue areas on Figure 17B-2 provided in the Data section.

Data

Sketch and label the white, pink, and blue areas on the drawing below.

(Answers may vary.)

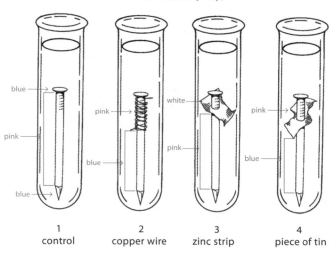

17B-2   Nails prepared for corrosion experiment

A fifth nail could be tested. If a nail is bent and placed in an agar solution in a petri dish, the potassium ferricyanide will turn blue at the head, the bent portion, and the tip. This indicates that pitting will occur at places of stress.

Blue indicates the oxidation of the iron atom to the Fe^{2+} ion. If there is no blue present, then iron is not corroding.

Analysis

1. Test tube 1
   a. Did iron corrode in test tube 1? _yes_
   b. How do you know?

      The ferricyanide indicator turned blue to show that Fe^{2+} ions formed.

2. Test tube 2
   a. Where is the pink color? _around the copper wire_
   b. What ions must be present there? _OH^- ions_
   c. Is the copper or the iron corroding? How can you tell?

      The iron is corroding; Fe^{2+} ions are forming, as indicated by the blue color.

   d. Does copper protect iron? _no_

3. Test tube 3
   a. Did iron corrode in test tube 3? _no_
   b. Does zinc protect iron? _yes_
   c. What ions were present in test tube 3?

      OH^- ions. Zn^{2+} ions also form but precipitate as white $Zn_3(Fe[CN]_6)_2$.

4. Test tube 4
   a. Which metal corroded in test tube 4? _iron_
   b. Does tin protect iron? _no_

5. Why did you add salt (NaCl) to the agar suspension?

   The salt speeds up the corrosion process by acting as an electrolyte and allowing charge to flow more easily.

6. Based on what you learned about the activity series for metals in Chapter 8 of your text, are the results you obtained in this lab what you expected? Explain.

   Yes. Both copper and tin are lower in the activity series than iron and are therefore less easily oxidized than iron; zinc is more active than iron and is therefore more easily oxidized than iron, thereby protecting it.

18A Models of Organic Compounds

Prelab

Concepts

Historically, scientists defined compounds extracted from animal or vegetable sources as **organic**. These compounds have one thing in common: they all contain carbon. Today most carbon-containing compounds are considered organic whether they come from synthetic or living ("organic") sources.

Organic compounds are classified according to certain structural features or groups of atoms contained in their compounds. These groups are known as **functional groups**, and they give organic compounds their characteristic physical and chemical properties. Some common functional groups are listed on page 462 in your text. You will make models of some of these compounds to help you recognize major functional groups.

You will also notice on page 462 that structural formulas, not molecular formulas, represent the compounds. Molecular formulas are not detailed enough to describe organic compounds completely. For example, a glucose molecule has the molecular formula $C_6H_{12}O_6$, but so do a number of other organic compounds, such as gulose and mannose. Each of these sugars is a completely different compound with its own set of properties, yet they all share the same molecular formula. Compounds with the same molecular formula but different structural formulas are called **isomers**. You will make models of some isomers to help you visualize the differences in structure.

Checkup

1. What is the old definition for *organic*? What is the current definition?

   Originally the word *organic* referred to any compound that

   came from a living (organic) source. Today it refers to most

   carbon-containing compounds.

2. What are isomers?

   compounds with the same molecular formula but different

   structural formulas

3. Draw the structural formulas for a pair of compounds that are isomers in the space provided.

Goals

✓ Explore the concept of isomerism with models.

✓ Recognize the major functional groups of organic compounds from models.

Materials

clay

toothpicks

Materials

Foam balls can be used instead of clay. It is probably best, if possible, to purchase inexpensive molecular model kits from a science supplier. Molecular model kits will have the correct three-dimensional shapes and angles.

Even if you do not perform this as a lab exercise, it is valuable as a homework assignment.

A classification system is needed because carbon atoms covalently bond with each other to form straight chains or rings that branch, may contain double and triple bonds, or may have other elements covalently bonded in place of hydrogen.

Show the students how to count the longest continuous chain. For example, if anything that they think is an isomer of C_3H_8 has three continuous carbons, then it is not an isomer.

4. Label the following pairs of structural formulas as either identical compounds, isomers, or unrelated compounds.

a. $-C-C-C-C-$ isomers

b. $-C-C-C-$ identical compounds

c. $-C-C-C$ unrelated compounds

d. $-C-C-C-C-OH$ isomers

5. Circle and name the functional groups in the following compounds. Use the chart in your text, page 462.

a. $-C-C-C-C-$ (OH)   alcohol

c. $-C-C-C-C$ carboxylic acid

b. $-C-C-C$ amide

d. $-C-C-O-C-C-$ ether

Procedure

1. Form models and derive structural formulas of hydrocarbons.

    a. Alkanes

    C_3H_8. Make a model of C_3H_8 and draw the structural formula corresponding to your model. (Record: 1a.) Try to rearrange the three carbon atoms and eight hydrogen atoms to form a different compound. Draw the structural formulas corresponding to any different arrangements you find. (Record: 1a.)

    C_4H_{10}. Make two different models of C_4H_{10} and draw the structural formulas. (Record: 1a.)

    b. Alkenes

    C_2H_4. Make a model of C_2H_4 and draw the structural formula. (Record: 1b.)

C₄H₈. Make models of two structures, each with the formula C_4H_8. Each model should have a chain of four carbons with no branches and no rings. Draw structural formulas of your models. (Record: 1b.) Construct a model of a branched isomer of C_4H_8. Draw the structural formula. (Record: 1b.) Attempt to construct another branched isomer of C_4H_8. (Record: 1b.)

  c. Alkynes

    C₂H₂. Make a model of C_2H_2. Draw the structural formula. (Record: 1c.)

2. Construct models for the compounds containing oxygen or nitrogen. Draw structural formulas for these models. (Record: 2–3.)

Data

Draw structural formulas in the space provided for each of these compounds.

Structural Formula

1. Hydrocarbons

  a. Alkanes

    C_3H_8

    C_4H_{10}

  b. Alkenes

    C_2H_4

    C_4H_8 (straight)

    C_4H_8 (branched)

    C_4H_8 (branched isomer)   No other isomers are possible.

  c. Alkynes

    C_2H_2

2. Organic compounds containing oxygen

  a. Alcohols

    C_2H_6O

  b. Ethers

    C_2H_6O

The OH can be in any position on either carbon.

c. Aldehydes

C_2H_4O

$$-\overset{|}{\underset{|}{C}}-\overset{O}{\overset{||}{C}}-$$

d. Ketones

C_3H_6O

$$-\overset{|}{\underset{|}{C}}-\overset{O}{\overset{||}{C}}-\overset{|}{\underset{|}{C}}-$$

e. Carboxylic acids

$C_2H_4O_2$

$$-\overset{|}{\underset{|}{C}}-\overset{O}{\overset{||}{C}}-OH$$

f. Esters

$C_2H_4O_2$

$$\overset{O}{\overset{||}{-C}}-O-\overset{|}{\underset{|}{C}}-$$

3. Organic compounds containing nitrogen

a. Amines

CH_5N

$$-\overset{|}{\underset{|}{C}}-\overset{|}{\underset{|}{N}}-$$

b. Amides

C_2H_5NO

$$-\overset{|}{\underset{|}{C}}-\overset{O}{\overset{||}{C}}-\overset{|}{\underset{|}{N}}- \quad \text{or} \quad -\overset{O}{\overset{||}{C}}-\overset{|}{\underset{|}{N}}-\overset{|}{\underset{|}{C}}-$$

c. Amino acids

$C_2H_5NO_2$

$$-\overset{|}{\underset{\underset{|}{N-}}{C}}-\overset{O}{\overset{||}{C}}-OH$$

Analysis

1. Compare the structures for the alcohol and ether that you constructed. What are the differences? What are the similarities? Differences: The oxygen atom is in a different location, or the atoms are connected in a different order. Similarities: Both structures have the same number of each type of element.

2. What structural feature distinguishes an aldehyde from a ketone? The ketone has an alkyl group instead of a hydrogen atom attached to the carbon with the doubly bonded oxygen.

3. Compare the structures of the carboxylic acid and ester that you constructed. What are the differences? What are the similarities? Differences: The hydrogen of the hydroxyl group in the acid is replaced by a methyl group on the ester. Similarities: Both structures contain the same number and type of elements.

4. What structural feature distinguishes an amide from an amine? An amine has one or more alkyl groups replacing one or more of the hydrogen atoms that are attached to the nitrogen of ammonia, whereas the amide has a nitrogen in the place of the hydroxyl group of a carboxylic acid; amines are structurally similar to ammonia, whereas amides are structurally similar to acids.

5. The properties of an amino acid would probably resemble the properties of what two types of compounds? amines and carboxylic acids

There are primary (1°), secondary (2°), and tertiary (3°) amines. A primary amine has one of the hydrogens, which is attached to the nitrogen of ammonia, replaced with an alkyl group; a secondary has two hydrogens replaced, and a tertiary has three. This system is also used for alcohols. The hydrogens that are replaced in an alcohol are bonded to the carbon atom that has the hydroxyl group.

The students will not find amino acids on the chart in the text. Amino acids are discussed in Section 18E. With a hint, they can figure it out. Tell them that the nitrogen is attached to the carbon that is bonded to the carboxylic acid group.

An amine can have from one to three hydrogen atoms replaced with alkyl groups.

18B The Synthesis of Soap

Prelab

Concepts

Early soap makers produced soap by basically the same saponification reaction that is used today. That is, they heated a fat with a metal hydroxide to produce a fatty acid salt (soap) and glycerin (or glycerol). Originally wood and plant ashes were the sources of the potassium compounds (KOH and K_2CO_3) used in the reaction; today NaOH is used. The following reaction shows this saponification process:

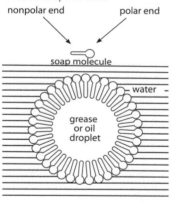

18B-1 Saponification reaction

The soap-making process has been known for at least twenty-three hundred years. Prior to AD 100, soap was used as a medicine, but since that time it has been used primarily for washing and cleaning. Soap, when suspended in water, removes dirt from surfaces. This cleaning power is the result of the structure of soap. Soap has a nonpolar end that dissolves in oil or grease droplets, and it has a polar carboxylate end that is attracted to polar water molecules. As the soap molecules align themselves around a droplet, they form a "coating." Once coated, the oil or grease can be washed away with water.

18B-2 The cleansing action of soap

Goals

✓ Synthesize soap by the same reaction historically used to produce it.

✓ Compare the behavior of soap and detergent in hard water.

Materials

balance
beakers, 150 mL and 250 mL
Bunsen burner
calcium chloride ($CaCl_2$) solution
ethyl alcohol (C_2H_5OH)
glass stirring rod
graduated cylinder, 10 mL
hydrochloric acid (HCl), 6 *M*
ice
iron (III) chloride ($FeCl_3$) solution
iron ring
lard or cottonseed oil
magnesium chloride ($MgCl_2$) solution
matches
mineral oil
phenolphthalein solution
ring stand
rubber stoppers, 2
sodium chloride (NaCl)
sodium hydroxide (NaOH), 6 *M*
synthetic detergent
test tube rack
test tubes, 6
wire gauze

The reason that bases feel slippery is that the alkaline salt saponifies fatty acids from the surface of the skin.

The solubility of soap is greatly reduced by the iron, calcium, and magnesium salts that are present in hard water. Soap in hard water forms insoluble metal carboxylates with these ions (the "ring" in the bathtub), whereas synthetic detergents do not. For this reason, detergents are often used in place of soap. Synthetic detergents—sulfonic acid salts—are similar to soap in structure but have a higher solubility in hard water.

18B-3   A typical synthetic detergent

Checkup

1. Although the saponification reaction used historically is basically the same as the one used today, there is a difference in the source of the chemicals. Name that difference.

   In the past the metal hydroxide came from the potassium
   compounds of wood and plant ashes; now it comes from NaOH.

2. In this experiment, how will you get the soap to form a solid that you can isolate from the solution?

   We will "salt it out" by adding a saturated NaCl solution.

3. How does soap "clean"?

   The soap molecules surround an oil or grease droplet because
   their nonpolar ends dissolve in the droplet and their carboxylate ends are attracted to water. The coated droplet can then
   be washed away with water.

4. What advantage does a detergent have over a soap?

   Detergents are more soluble than soap in hard water.

Procedure

Part A: Synthesizing Soap

1. Put 10 g of lard or cottonseed oil in a 250 mL beaker. Add 10 mL of ethyl alcohol and 15 mL of 6 *M* NaOH. Adding the alcohol to the fat-NaOH mixture increases the solubility of the mixture, thereby speeding up the saponification.

2. Attach an iron ring to your ring stand and place a wire gauze on it. Place your beaker containing the fat mixture on the gauze and heat the mixture *gently* with a low flame while stirring it until you no longer detect the odor of alcohol above the beaker. A pasty product, soap, will be left. (*Note*: Keep the flame away from the top of the beaker. The alcohol could burn as it evaporates. If it does catch fire, cover the beaker with a watch glass.)

3. While the soap is cooling, saturate 50 mL of distilled water with NaCl in a 150 mL beaker.

4. When the soap is cool, add the saturated salt solution and stir it thoroughly. This process is called "salting out" and will precipitate the soap.

5. Hold back the soap with a stirring rod and decant the liquid. Rinse the soap with several portions of ice water, and press the soap into a cake.

Part B: Testing the Soap

1. Take a small amount of your soap and wash your hands with it. How does it feel? How does it work? (Record: 1.)

2. Compare the cleaning abilities of soap and detergent.

   a. Add ten drops of mineral oil and 10 mL of water to three test tubes. Set two tubes aside. Insert a stopper in the third test tube and shake it. An emulsion or suspension of tiny droplets of mineral oil in water will form. Let it stand for a few minutes and record your observations. (Record: 2a.)

   b. To the two tubes that you set aside, add about 0.5 g of your soap to one and about 0.5 g of a synthetic detergent to the other. Stopper both and shake well. Record your observations of the soap and the detergent additions. (Record: 2b–c.)

3. Compare the solubilities of soap and detergent salts.

   a. Take about 1 g of your soap and add it to 30 mL of water in a 150 mL beaker. Dissolve the soap by warming the solution gently while stirring. Pour equal volumes of the soap solution into three test tubes. Then add five drops of 0.1 M $CaCl_2$ to the first test tube, five drops of 0.1 M $MgCl_2$ to the second, and five drops of 0.1 M $FeCl_3$ to the third. Note the results. (Record: 3.)

   b. Repeat Step 3a for a synthetic detergent. (Record: 3.)

4. Test the acids of the soap and detergent.

   a. Dissolve another gram of your soap in 20 mL of water. Place a few drops of phenolphthalein solution in the soap solution as an acid-base indicator. Add 6 M HCl dropwise until the solution is acidic (colorless). The reaction converts the fatty acid salts (soaps) to the fatty acids that were contained in the fat. Are fatty acids soluble in water? (Record: 4.)

   b. Repeat Step 4a for a synthetic detergent. (Record: 5.)

Data

1. How did your soap feel? How did it work?

   It felt slippery. It did not work very well, but it did produce

   some suds.

2. Compare the cleaning ability of soap and detergent.

Explain that *saturate* means to add as much salt as the water will dissolve.

The soap precipitates because of the common ion effect.

Because the NaOH is in excess, make sure that the students rinse the soap well. The students will calculate that the NaOH is in excess in the Analysis section.

Vegetable oil will also work.

Remind the students to use distilled water for this procedure.

If the students do not have three transfer pipets, be sure that they rinse the one pipet between uses, or you may wish to have these solutions available in plastic dropper bottles.

Students may need to heat the solution to dissolve the soap.

Answers will vary, but the detergent should perform better.

a. Describe the emulsion of mineral oil in water.

Some fine droplets of mineral oil are suspended in water;

most of the mineral oil separates to form a layer on top.

b. Describe the emulsion of mineral oil and soap in water.

fewer droplets of mineral oil

c. Describe the emulsion of mineral oil and detergent in water.

no observable mineral oil

3. Compare the solubilities of soap and detergent in the presence of salts by filling in the following chart.

	Soap	Detergent
$CaCl_2$		
$MgCl_2$		
$FeCl_3$		

4. Was the fatty acid produced by the reaction of acid and soap soluble in water? __no__

5. Was the sulfonic acid formed from the detergent soluble in water?

yes

Analysis

1. Which had the better cleaning action—the soap or the detergent? __the detergent__

2. Using the information in the Concepts section, explain the results in Step 3 of the Data section.

The detergent does not form insoluble salts in hard water (water with dissolved iron, calcium, or magnesium

salts); it has a higher solubility.

3. In conclusion, what advantages do you think detergents have over soaps?

Detergents dissolve better and do not precipitate in either hard or acidic water; therefore, they clean better

under all conditions.

4. A mole of fat has a gram-molecular mass of about 900 g, and a mole of NaOH has a gram-molecular mass of 40 g. Which reactant was in excess in the reaction you carried out in Step A1 of the Procedure section? (*Hint*: The following steps will help you. You should first calculate the number of moles of fat and NaOH used in Procedure A1.)

$$\frac{10 \text{ g fat}}{} \times \frac{1 \text{ mol fat}}{900 \text{ g fat}} = \text{moles of fat}$$

$$\frac{15 \text{ mL}}{} \times \frac{1 \text{ L}}{1000 \text{ mL}} \times \frac{6 \text{ mol NaOH}}{1 \text{ L}} = \text{moles NaOH}$$

Then you should compare the moles calculated to the mole-to-mole ratio of the balanced equation in the Concepts section.

The NaOH is in excess. (The calculated mole-to-mole ratio is 0.01 mol fat : 0.09 mol NaOH. The theoretical

ratio is 1 mol fat : 3 mol NaOH. Therefore, three times more NaOH was used than was necessary.)

18C Carbohydrates, Proteins, and Fats in Foods

Prelab

Concepts

Carbohydrates, proteins, and fats make up the bulk of the biomolecules found in the foods we eat. Milk—sometimes considered a complete food—contains all three of these groups. Carbohydrates include both the polysaccharides, such as starch and cellulose, and the simpler molecules, such as sucrose, lactose, and glucose. Proteins are large molecules that are composed of amino acids chemically joined by what are called *peptide bonds*. The major protein in milk is casein, but milk also contains the proteins albumin and globulin. Both solid fat and liquid oil are included in the category of fats. Whole milk has a fat content of about 4% and contains a variety of fat molecules. Many other familiar foods besides milk contain more than one of these classes of molecules.

In this lab, you will test for starch (a polysaccharide carbohydrate) by its reaction with iodine to form a dark blue complex molecule—the one you saw in Lab 17A. Monosaccharides and disaccharides that have a free aldehyde functional group can be detected by their reaction with a solution of copper (II) sulfate to form a brick red precipitate of copper (I) oxide. Sugars that react in this way are known as *reducing sugars*. Proteins will be detected by the interaction of their peptide groups with copper (II) ions in basic solution to form a violet color (it can sometimes be pink); molecules with two or more peptide bonds will give a positive result. This test is called the *biuret test*. Fats will be detected by a simple test known as the grease spot test. Foods containing fat will produce a translucent spot on filter paper when they come into contact with it.

Checkup

1. Why is acetone used for the fat test instead of water? (*Hint*: Compare the properties of fat, acetone, and water.)

   Acetone is less polar than water and will dissolve some of the

   nonpolar fat from the food better than water.

2. What will you observe in a positive test for protein in a food?

   The mixture will turn violet or pink.

3. What *color change* will you observe in a positive test for reducing sugars? The Benedict's reagent will change from blue to

   brick red (or brown or yellow).

4. What is the purpose for using distilled water as one of the test liquids in the tests for starch, reducing sugars, and protein?

   It serves as a blank so that you can tell what a negative test

   looks like.

5. What functional group is the Benedict's reagent detecting? the biuret test? aldehyde; peptide bonds

Goals

✓ Detect the presence of carbohydrates, proteins, and fats in milk.

✓ Detect the presence of sugar, starch, protein, and fat in other foods.

Materials

acetone
balance
beaker, 150 mL, 2
beaker, 250 mL
Benedict's reagent
boiling stones
Bunsen burner
copper (II) sulfate solution, 2%
filter paper
food to be tested
gelatin suspension, 1%
glucose solution, 1%
graduated cylinder, 10 mL
iodine solution
iron ring
matches
milk
mortar and pestle
ring stand
sodium hydroxide (NaOH), 6 *M*
starch suspension, 1%
test tube rack
test tubes, 12
transfer pipet (eyedropper)
vegetable oil
wire gauze

Materials

Benedict's reagent may be purchased or prepared as follows: While heating, dissolve 51.9 g trisodium citrate monohydrate and 30 g anhydrous sodium carbonate in 200 mL distilled water. Dissolve 1.73 g copper (II) sulfate pentahydrate in 30 mL distilled water and add it to the first solution. Dilute to 300 mL with distilled water.

Prepare the iodine solution as follows: Dissolve 1 g I_2 and 2 g KI in approximately 10 mL distilled water; dilute to 100 mL and store in a tightly stoppered bottle. Add sufficient quantities of this stock solution to distilled water to produce an amber or pale orange test solution.

Soften the required amount of gelatin in 3–4 mL of cool, distilled water; bring to boiling the remainder of the water needed, and then add the softened gelatin to it, heating until the mixture is clear.

Prepare the starch suspension as follows: Make a paste of the measured amount of starch using 3–4 mL of the needed water, bring the remainder of the water to boiling, and then add the paste to it, heating until it is clear.

Whole milk will work best because it has more fat.

Suggested foods include crackers, fruit, and nuts.

Procedure

1. Test for fats in milk.

   a. Apply one drop of vegetable oil to a piece of filter paper, about an inch from the edge. This should produce a translucent spot that is visible when you hold the paper up to a light, even when it is dry. Label this spot "oil." Use this as your reference for the grease spot test.

   b. Apply 2 drops of milk to the same piece of filter paper used in Step 1a. Assuming that the oil spot is in the "12 o'clock" position, apply the milk at the "4 o'clock" position. Label this spot "milk." Set the filter paper aside to dry completely before comparing the milk spot to the oil spot. (Record: 1.) You may hasten the drying, if necessary, by using a hair dryer to dry the paper.

2. Test for carbohydrates in milk.

   a. First, set up your ring stand for a boiling water bath, using your 250 mL beaker half full of water. Begin heating the water so that it is ready when you need it in Step 2b. Add 2–3 boiling stones to the beaker for more even boiling. You will test for the presence of the polysaccharide starch as follows: In one clean test tube, place 1 mL (20 drops) of distilled water; in a second clean test tube, place 1 mL (20 drops) of 1% starch suspension; and in a third clean test tube, place 1 mL (20 drops) of milk. Add 1–2 drops of iodine solution to each tube and agitate them to mix. Compare your results for milk to that for the blank (water) and the control (starch). Does milk contain starch? (Record: 2.)

   b. Test for the presence of simple sugars. In separate, clean, labeled test tubes, place 1 mL (20 drops) of each of the following: distilled water in tube 1, 1% glucose in tube 2, and milk in tube 3. To each tube add 5 mL of Benedict's reagent, mix well, and place them all in a boiling water bath for 5–10 minutes. (Proceed to the next step during this time.) The formation of a brick red or brown (sometimes yellow) precipitate is considered a positive test for reducing sugars. Water serves as your blank and the glucose solution serves as your positive reference. (Not all positive tests need be as red as the one obtained with glucose, however.) Does milk contain reducing sugars? (Record: 3.)

3. Test for proteins in milk.

   a. Add 1 mL (20 drops) of each of the following liquids to clean, separate, labeled tubes: distilled water in tube 1, 1% gelatin in tube 2, and milk in tube 3.

   b. To each tube, add 5 drops of 6 M NaOH and 3 drops of 2% copper (II) sulfate solution. Mix each tube by agitating it. Allow to stand for 3–5 minutes. Compare the color produced (if any) in milk with that produced in each of the other tubes. Do not mistake the deepening of the blue copper (II) ion that occurs in basic solutions for a change to violet. A positive test is a violet or pink coloration. Does milk contain protein? (Record: 4.)

4. Test for fats, carbohydrates, and proteins in another food.

a. *If the food to be tested is a solid*, weigh out about a 2-gram sample of it and place it in a mortar. If it contains large pieces, grind it into small pieces with the pestle. Add about 5 mL of acetone and continue to carefully grind the food for about one minute. Allow the mixture to settle for several minutes, and then carefully decant the liquid into a 150 mL beaker and set it aside. Add 1–2 grams of clean sand to the residue in the mortar and continue grinding the food as you gradually add 10–15 mL of distilled water. Grind thoroughly until you have a well-pulverized food suspension.

b. Decant the suspension into a second clean 150 mL beaker, leaving the sand and any unsuspended residue in the mortar.

c. Perform the protein test as follows: Measure about 1 mL of the food suspension into a clean test tube, add 5 drops of 6 M NaOH and 3 drops of 2% $CuSO_4$, and then mix and allow to stand for several minutes. Compare your results with those obtained in Step 3b. (Record: 5.)

d. Heat the food suspension in the beaker to a gentle boil, using your burner; allow to cool.

e. While the boiled food suspension is cooling, perform the fat test by adding 2 drops of the acetone solution from Step 4a to the piece of filter paper from Step 1, this time at the "8 o'clock" position. Allow it to dry partially before repeating with two more drops. When it is completely dry, compare your results with the grease spot test in Step 1a. (Record: 6.)

f. Perform the reducing sugars test by mixing about 1 mL of the boiled suspension with 5 mL of Benedict's reagent in a clean test tube; place it in a boiling water bath for 5–10 minutes. Compare your results with those for the blank and the known reducing sugar in Step 2b. (Record: 7.)

g. Determine whether there is starch in your food sample by adding 1–3 drops of iodine solution to about 1 mL of the boiled suspension in a clean test tube. Report the absence or presence of starch. (Record: 8.)

h. *If the food to be tested is a liquid*, use it wherever a food suspension is called for in the procedure above, in Steps c, f, and g. Perform the fat test by using the original liquid food in place of the acetone solution in Step e.

i. Be sure to clean all your glassware with detergent when you are finished.

Data

1. Fat test

   Appearance of oil spot:

   It appears translucent.

   Appearance of milk spot:

   It appears translucent, but not as much as the oil.

2. Starch test

Sample	Color with iodine
Distilled water	pale yellow
1% starch suspension	dark blue
Milk	yellow orange

3. Reducing sugar test

Sample	Color after heating
Distilled water	blue
1% glucose	brick red
Milk	brick red

4. Protein test

Sample	Color with reagent
Distilled water	blue
1% gelatin	violet
Milk	violet

Food description: _____

5. Protein test observations:

_____

6. Fat test observations:

_____

7. Reducing sugar test observations:

_____

8. Starch test observations:

_____

Analysis

1. What do you conclude about the presence of fat, starch, reducing sugar, and protein in milk? Support *each* conclusion with observations from your data.

   Answers for fat will vary with the type of milk used (those that have fat should mention the translucent spot),

   but milk does not contain starch (no dark blue color with iodine), does contain reducing sugar (brick red

   precipitate), and does contain protein (violet color in biuret test).

2. What do you conclude about the presence of fat, starch, reducing sugar, and protein in the food that you analyzed? Support each conclusion with observations from your data.

   Answers will vary with the food, but check prepared food containers or nutrition texts for the answers. Small

   amounts of a given type of food class may not show up in these tests.

   _____

19 Identification of Plastics

Prelab

Concepts

Plastics are virtually everywhere in our modern environment. Their properties vary widely, as do their uses. Some are hard and rigid while others are very flexible, some melt easily while others resist high temperatures, and some are transparent while others are opaque or translucent. They range in uses from car parts to clothing we wear, from food and beverage containers to utensils used for eating, and from grocery bags to shampoo bottles. Their uses often stem from their physical properties, which, in turn, are a result of their chemical structure.

Since plastics are generally very unreactive chemically, they do not degrade ("break down") easily when disposed of in a landfill and may remain there unchanged for many years. As a result of their longevity, a greater emphasis has recently been placed on recycling plastics instead of disposing of them by burning or landfilling them. Some are recycled by being used in a totally different application; others are melted down and reused in similar or identical ways; some are not recyclable. Since there are so many types of plastics in use and different methods of recycling are used for each, they need to be separated from one another according to type.

In this lab, you will use density as the principal method to differentiate between the six common types of plastic, shown in Table 19-1. One test will be a chemical test that is based on the fact that one of the plastics contains chlorine. You will use what you learn from known samples of plastic to identify an unknown sample of plastic.

Goals

✓ Determine the relative densities of plastics to aid in their identification.

✓ Identify the type of plastic in an unknown plastic sample.

Materials

beaker, 150 mL

Bunsen burner

copper wire, 5"

cork, large

corn oil

isopropyl alcohol solution, 45.5%

marker, fine tip, permanent ink (optional)

matches

plastic samples

salt water (NaCl), saturated

tweezers (or crucible tongs)

19-1 Plastic Recycling Codes

Recycling number	Abbreviation	Polymer name	Density (in g/cm³)
1	PET(E)	polyethylene terephthalate	1.38–1.39
2	HDPE	high-density polyethylene	0.94–0.96
3	PVC or V	polyvinyl chloride	1.32–1.42
4	LDPE	low-density polyethylene	0.91–0.93
5	PP	polypropylene	0.90–0.92
6	PS or S	polystyrene	1.03–1.06

Checkup

1. What is the name of the plastic that contains the element chlorine?

   polyvinyl chloride

Materials

Dilute 45.5 mL of pure propan-2-ol (isopropyl alcohol) to 100.0 mL with deionized water or dilute 65.0 mL of rubbing alcohol (70% by volume) to 100.0 mL; check this with your samples of HDPE, LDPE, and PP prior to lab to be sure it works.

If you choose to use any other type of vegetable oil, try it first to be sure its density permits clearly distinguishing between PP and LDPE.

Eighteen-gauge wire works well; if it is too thin, it doesn't handle well and may melt.

You should be able to find containers around your home that are composed of the six common plastics. Unknowns should preferably be of different colors or appearance from the known plastic samples so as not to confuse them with the knowns or to make their identity obvious. For example, shampoo bottles are composed of at least three different types of plastic, depending on the brand, and come in a variety of colors. Approximately 0.5 cm squares of each type are sufficient for each group. You may wish to assign either one or two unknowns.

2. What property will you use to identify the majority of the plastic samples? _density_

3. If you owned a plastics recycling business that accepted primarily milk jugs and soft drink bottles, would you be able to separate them without handling each piece? Explain. (You may use the information from Table 19-1 and from the uses of plastics discussed in your textbook.)

Yes. Since milk jugs are HDPE with a density range of 0.94–0.96 g/cm³ and soft drink bottles are PET(E) with a density range of 1.38–1.39 g/cm³, simply placing them in a large tank of water would segregate them; the HDPE would float and the PET(E) would sink.

4. Which would be a better choice of plastic for the ropes used as lane markers in a swimming pool—PVC or PP? Explain your reasoning.

PP would be better because it is less dense than water, whereas PVC is more dense; you would want the rope to float if it is to be used as a lane marker.

Procedure

1. Obtain one sample of each type of plastic, known and unknown. If they are not easily distinguishable from one another, make small identifying numbers or letters, using the felt tip pen provided. Describe your samples. (Record: 1.)

2. Fill your 150 mL beaker about half full with tap water. Place all of your plastic samples in the beaker, and stir with a stirring rod to overcome surface tension and to dislodge any air bubbles from the samples; note which ones float and which sink. Record your observations. (Record: 2.)

3. Using tweezers or tongs, remove all of your samples from the water and dry them with a paper towel; set aside those that floated to work with later. Empty the water from the beaker and allow it to drain. Insert the copper wire into the cork to a depth of about one-half inch. While holding the cork as a handle, heat the free end of the wire in a well-adjusted burner flame until it no longer gives a green color to the flame. While it is still hot, touch the end to one of the plastic samples that sank in the water. This will melt a small amount of the plastic onto the wire; insert it again into the flame and note the color produced. (See Figure 19-1.) Do not put the entire plastic sample in the flame! Plastics that contain chlorine will produce a green flame; those that do not will burn with a yellow color. Repeat this procedure for each of your samples that sank in water. (Record: 3.) (From here on, you will need to fill in only the appropriate parts of the Data table; write *N/A* in the other blocks.)

A beaker smaller than 150 mL (e.g., 50 mL) is preferable because smaller volumes of liquid are needed. This size was chosen because it is the smallest size used for other labs.

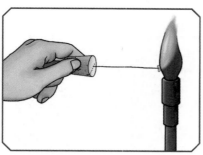

19-1   Copper wire test

4. Obtain about 40 mL of saturated salt water in your 150 mL beaker. Select the plastic samples that did *not* float in water or turn the flame green and place them in the salt water. Stir to dislodge any bubbles and note whether they sink or float. (Record: 4.)

5. Return the salt water to the original container unless your teacher tells you otherwise. Rinse your beaker well and allow it to drain thoroughly. Then obtain about 50 mL of the alcohol solution in your beaker and place the plastic samples that floated in water into the alcohol solution. Stir with a clean stirring rod and note the behavior of each. (Record: 5.) Return the alcohol solution to its original container unless directed otherwise by your teacher.

6. Rinse your beaker and dry it well with a paper towel. Then obtain about 50 mL of corn oil in the beaker. Take the plastic samples that floated in the alcohol solution and put them in the oil. Push them under the surface of the oil with a dry stirring rod and allow them to come to rest; observe whether they float or sink in the oil. (Record: 6.) Return the oil to the original container (unless otherwise instructed). Discard all of your plastic samples in the trash and clean the oily beaker well with hot, soapy water.

7. Fill in the flow chart in the Analysis section with the appropriate plastic type and answer the questions.

Data

Plastic ID	1. Color, description	2. Behavior in water	3. Copper wire test	4. Behavior in salt water	5. Behavior in alcohol solution	6. Behavior in corn oil
PET(E), 1	Answers will vary.	sinks	yellow	sinks	N/A	N/A
HDPE, 2		floats	N/A	N/A	sinks	N/A
PVC (V), 3		sinks	green	N/A	N/A	N/A
LDPE, 4		floats	N/A	N/A	floats	sinks
PP, 5		floats	N/A	N/A	floats	floats
PS (S), 6		sinks	yellow	floats	N/A	N/A
Unknown						

Analysis

1. Fill in the following flow chart with the appropriate symbol for each plastic, using your data table.

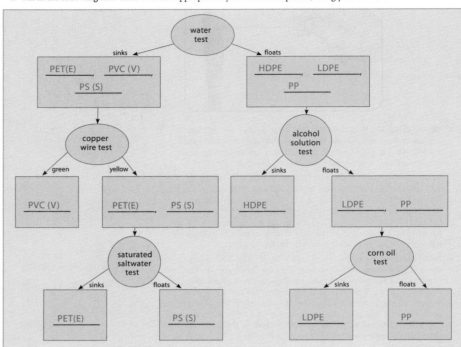

2. Tell the identity of your unknown. Explain your reasoning.

Answers will vary.

3. From the results you observed, which plastic was the densest? Did this agree with the data in Table 19-1?

PET(E); yes

4. Why was it necessary to use the copper wire test to discriminate one of the plastics from the others?

Its density was so close to that of another plastic that it might be hard to tell them apart on the basis of the float test.

5. Why was it important to completely dry each piece of plastic between the different float tests?

If there were still some liquid droplets on the plastic, they might affect whether it sinks or floats.

Materials

The Handbook of Chemistry and Physics, edited by David R. Lide, contains a table of the isotopes that provides all the necessary information.

20 Mass Defect and Binding Energy

Prelab

Concepts

A fundamental idea of modern nuclear chemistry is that mass and energy are equivalent. Mass can be changed into energy, and energy can be changed into mass. The equivalence of mass and energy seems to be responsible for the force that holds a nucleus together. Within each nucleus there are protons and neutrons. It seems that protons, with their similar positive charges, should repel each other and fly away from the nucleus. Yet the protons remain, held by some strong force.

Scientists have observed that atoms have less mass than expected and that the missing mass is proportional to the force required to hold the particles in each nucleus together. The missing mass is called the **mass defect**, and the force that holds each nucleus together is called the **nuclear binding energy**. The equation $E = mc^2$ relates the quantities of mass and energy (where E is nuclear binding energy, m is the mass defect, and c is the speed of light).

The relationship between mass and energy is also seen in nuclear reactions. Here, a small amount of mass is converted into a large amount of energy. Again, the equation $E = mc^2$ describes the relationship between the quantities of mass and energy; E is the energy released, and m is the mass that is converted.

Goals

✓ Calculate the mass defect of given atoms.

✓ Determine the binding energy per nuclear particle for given nuclei.

✓ Use the equation $E = mc^2$ in conversions between mass and energy.

Material

reference source with precise masses of atoms

Checkup

1. What are the proper units for energy, mass, and the speed of light in the equation $E = mc^2$?

   energy—joules; mass—kilograms; speed of light—meters per

   second

2. How will you determine the theoretical mass of an atom?

   Add the masses of all the protons, neutrons, and electrons

   contained in it.

3. How will you determine the actual mass of an atom?

   by looking it up in a reference book

Procedure

In this exercise, you will calculate the binding energy per nuclear particle for He-4, Fe-56, and U-232 atoms. You will need to make several preliminary calculations for each atom.

1. The first step in the process is to calculate the theoretical mass of the atom. To do this, find the total mass of all the electrons, protons, and neutrons. Use the information that a proton is 1.0073 u, a neutron is 1.0087 u, and an electron is 0.00055 u. For example, Na-23 atoms have 11 protons, 11 electrons, and 12 neutrons. The theoretical mass of a Na-23 atom is 23.1908 u. (Only four decimal places are permitted based on significant digit rules.)

$$\frac{11 \ \text{protons} \ | \ 1.0073 \ \text{u}}{\text{proton}} = 11.0803 \ \text{u} \ (4 \ \text{decimal places})$$

$$\frac{12 \ \text{neutrons} \ | \ 1.0087 \ \text{u}}{\text{neutron}} = 12.1044 \ \text{u} \ (4 \ \text{decimal places})$$

$$\frac{11 \ \text{electrons} \ | \ 0.00055 \ \text{u}}{\text{electron}} = 0.00605 \ \text{u} \ (5 \ \text{decimal places})$$

$$\text{Total} = 23.1908 \ \text{u} \ (4 \ \text{decimal places})$$

2. You can use reference books to look up the actual masses of atoms. A reference source lists the mass of the Na-23 atom as 22.9898 u.

3. To find the mass defect for an atom, subtract the actual mass from the theoretical mass. For the Na-23 atom, the mass defect is 23.1908 − 22.9898, or 0.2010 u.

4. Convert the mass defect that is now in atomic mass units to units of kilograms. One u equals 1.66×10^{-27} kg. The mass defect of the Na-23 atom is 3.34×10^{-28} kg.

5. Express the mass defect as the binding energy, using $E = mc^2$. When the mass defect is expressed in kilograms, and the speed of light is in meters per second, this equation yields the binding energy in units called joules (J). For the Na-23 atom,
   $E = mc^2$
   $E = (3.34 \times 10^{-28} \ \text{kg})(3.00 \times 10^8 \ \text{m/s})^2$
   $E = 3.01 \times 10^{-11}$ J.

6. Calculate the binding energy per nuclear particle by dividing the binding energy by the number of particles in the nucleus. The Na-23 atom has 23 *nuclear* particles; its binding energy per particle is

$$\frac{3.01 \times 10^{-11} \ \text{J}}{23 \ \text{particles}}, \ \text{or} \ 1.31 \times 10^{-12} \ \text{J/particle}.$$

7. Plot the binding energy per nuclear particle on a graph for comparison to other atoms.

Data

Fill in the data values for each step of your calculation in the following table and plot your results on the graph.

	He-4	Na-23	Fe-56	U-232
Theoretical mass (u)	4.0331	23.1908	56.4651	233.9402
Actual mass (u)	4.00260	22.9898	55.9349	232.0372
Mass defect (u)	0.0305	0.2010	0.5302	1.9030
Mass defect (kg)	5.06×10^{-29}	3.34×10^{-28}	8.80×10^{-28}	3.16×10^{-27}
Binding energy (J)	4.56×10^{-12}	3.01×10^{-11}	7.92×10^{-11}	2.84×10^{-10}
Binding energy per nuclear particle (J/particle)	1.14×10^{-12}	1.31×10^{-12}	1.41×10^{-12}	1.22×10^{-12}

Joules can be converted to kilocalories:
1 kcal = 4184 J.

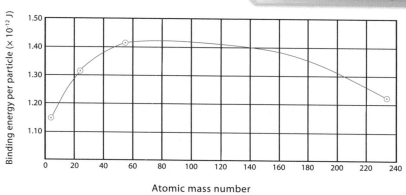

20-1   Graph of binding energy per particle
related to atomic mass number

Analysis

1. Which atom of those you worked with in this exercise had the greatest mass defect? the least?

   U-232; He-4

2. Which atom had the greatest binding energy? the least?

   U-232; He-4

3. Which atom had the greatest binding energy per particle? the least?

   Fe-56; He-4

4. Which of the atoms is the most stable?

   Fe-56

5. If helium atoms underwent fission and split apart into hydrogen atoms, would the process release or absorb energy? Why?

   The process would absorb energy because the atoms produced by such a process would have less binding

   energy per particle than the original helium atoms. Thus, they would be less stable. Or, it would require

   energy to overcome the binding energy holding the nuclear particles together.

6. A 20-megaton hydrogen bomb releases energy equivalent to that of the explosion of 20 million tons of TNT. Use the fact that 1 ton of TNT releases 10^6 kcal of energy to calculate how much matter is converted into energy in the thermonuclear explosion. (*Hints*: 1 kcal = 4184 J and 1 J = 1 kg · m²/s²)

   $$\frac{2 \times 10^7 \text{ tons TNT}}{} \left| \frac{10^6 \text{ kcal}}{1 \text{ ton TNT}} \right| \frac{4184 \text{ J}}{1 \text{ kcal}} = 8 \times 10^{16} \text{ J}$$

   $E = mc^2$

   $$m = \frac{E}{c^2} = \frac{8 \times 10^{16} \text{ J}}{(3 \times 10^8 \text{ m/s})^2} = 0.9 \text{ kg of matter}$$

Appendix A
Graphing Techniques

Constructing Graphs

When data are recorded in tables, it is difficult to see the relationship that exists between sets of numbers. To make trends and patterns easy to see, you will often put your data on a graph.

In experiments that search for a cause-effect relationship between two variables, you will cause one variable (the independent variable) to change and observe the effect on the second variable (the dependent variable). If you were to investigate how the solubility of NH_4Cl changes with temperature, temperature would be the independent variable, and solubility would be the dependent variable. Traditionally, the independent variable is plotted on the x-axis of the graph, and the dependent variable is plotted on the y-axis.

As you construct your graph, choose a scale that will show the plotted points clearly. Do not make the graph so small that the data cannot be clearly seen or so large that the graph will not fit on a single sheet of paper. Pick a scale that will conveniently include the entire range of each variable. The scales on each axis do not have to be the same. For instance, the scale on the x-axis might be 5 °C for every line, while the scale on the y-axis could be 2 g for every line. Your scale should be easy to subdivide. Subdivisions of 1, 2, 5, and 10 are the most convenient.

Once you have decided which variable will be plotted on which axis and the scales that will be used, neatly label the name of each quantity and the numbers on each axis. The title of the graph should be printed at the top of the graph. If more than one line will be sketched on the same graph, include some key that identifies each line. Plot each of your data points by making small dots and circling them. Next, draw a smooth line that connects all the data points. Figure 1 illustrates these techniques.

Observed Solubilities of NH_4Cl	
Temperature (°C)	Solubility (g/100 mL H_2O)
10	33
20	37
30	41
40	45
50	50
60	56

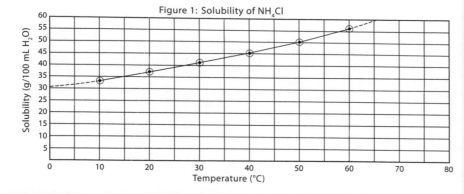

Figure 1: Solubility of NH_4Cl

Please refer to ALGEBRA 2 FOR CHRISTIAN SCHOOLS, Second Edition, for instructions on using a graphing calculator. Appendix D in the Teacher's Edition gives instructions for using a graphing calculator as well as the underlying principles involved.

In some cases, you will want to draw a straight line even though your data points do not fall precisely in a line. If this occurs, draw a line that shows the general relationship. Be sure to make the line go through the average values of the plotted points. The line in Figure 2A is incorrect because it lies above the cluster of points near the bottom of the graph and below the cluster of points at the top. Figure 2B shows the correct method of fitting a straight line to a series of points.

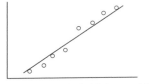 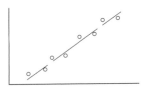

(A) incorrect method of fitting a straight line to a series of points

(B) correct method of fitting a straight line to a series of points

Figure 2

Interpreting Graphs

The shape of a graphed line tells much about the relationship between the variables. A straight line that rises from the origin indicates a direct relationship. A straight line that does not start at the origin shows that a linear relationship exists. A line that curves up (or down) from left to right indicates that the equation relating the two variables contains some exponent. A curved or straight line that is downward from left to right often describes an inverse relationship.

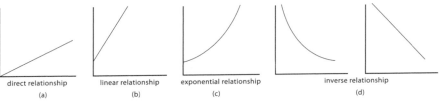

| direct relationship | linear relationship | exponential relationship | inverse relationship |
| (a) | (b) | (c) | (d) |

Figure 3: Typical graphs for different variable data relationships

Graphs can be used to predict additional data points that have not been experimentally determined. Assuming that points between verified data points are correct because they fall on the graphed line is called *interpolation*. From the graph of NH_4Cl solubilities (Figure 1), it is reasonable to assume that 43 g of NH_4Cl would dissolve at 35 °C. Extending the graphed line past the verified data points in either direction is called *extrapolation*. Extrapolations are usually indicated by dotted lines rather than by solid lines. The graph of NH_4Cl solubilities indicates that 59 g would dissolve at 65 °C. This extrapolation is reasonable, but it may not be totally accurate.

Extrapolation always introduces the element of uncertainty in scientific studies. Use this fact to discuss the ways in which extrapolation may be misused in our modern culture. Some examples are projected climate change and age-of-the-earth theories based on dating methods with limited reliability.

Appendix B
Laboratory Equipment

hanging-pan balance

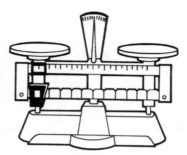
double-pan balance

electronic balance

beaker

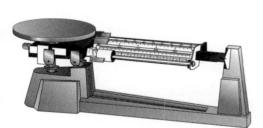
triple-beam balance

Bunsen burner

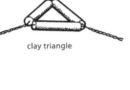

buret

buret clamp

filtering funnel

clay triangle

Erlenmeyer flask

crucible and cover

crucible tongs

evaporating dish

eyedropper

filter paper

iron ring

graduated cylinder

mortar and pestle

ring stand

rubber stoppers

pinchcock clamp

spatula

plastic transfer pipet

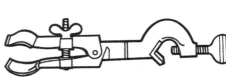

test tube brush

test tube clamp

test tube

test tube holder

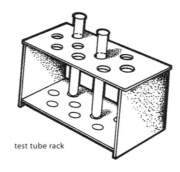

watch glass

test tube rack

wire gauze

wash bottle

Appendix C
Laboratory Techniques

Using Mechanical Balances

The masses of substances can be determined in the laboratory with the use of a mechanical balance. Several kinds of mechanical balances are common, but all of them operate on the same principles. To use a mechanical balance properly, follow the steps given below:

1. Place the balance on a smooth, level surface.

2. Keep the balance pan(s) clean and dry. Never put chemicals directly on the metal surface of the pan(s). Place materials on a sheet of filter paper, on a watch glass, or in a beaker.

3. Check the rest point of the empty balance. To do this, remove all weight from the pans and slide all movable masses to their zero positions. If the balance beam swings back and forth, note the central point of the swing. You do not have to wait until the beam stops swinging completely. If the central point lies more than two divisions from the marked zero point, have your teacher adjust the balance. Do NOT adjust the balance yourself!

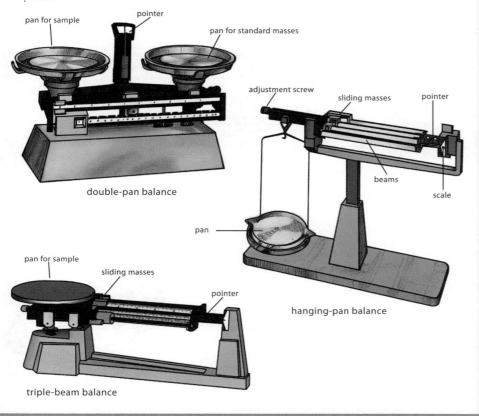

double-pan balance

hanging-pan balance

triple-beam balance

Students can practice these techniques by finding the mass of a paper towel, a sample of sand (on weighing paper), and a sample of liquid (in a graduated cylinder). Explain that the mass of any container used must be known in order to calculate the mass of the desired substance.

Double-Pan Balance

Always place the substance being weighed on the left pan. Put a standard mass that you judge to be slightly heavier than the substance being weighed on the right pan. If the mass is indeed heavier than the object, replace it with the next smaller mass. Place other smaller masses on the pan until the standards are as close as possible to, but not greater than, the mass of the sample. At this point, move the sliding mass (or masses) until the object is balanced. The sum of all the masses on the pan and on the slide's scale is the mass of the object.

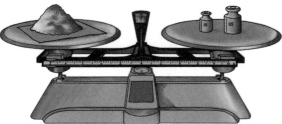

The mass of this substance is 40.00 g.

Triple-Beam Balance and Hanging-Pan Balance

Place the substance whose mass you are trying to find on the pan and adjust the sliding masses. Move the largest masses first, and then make final adjustments with the smaller masses. The sum of all the readings is the mass of the object.

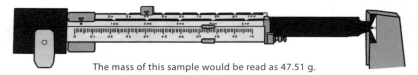

The mass of this sample would be read as 47.51 g.

Using an Electronic Balance

Electronic balances are generally faster and easier to use than their mechanical counterparts. To use an electronic balance properly, follow the instructions given below:

1. Make sure the balance is on a smooth, flat surface.

2. Turn the balance on and check to make sure there is a reading of 0.

3. Protect the balance pan by placing your sample carrier (weighing paper, watch glass, beaker, etc.) on the pan. Never put chemicals directly on the surface of the pan.

4. Record the weight of your sample carrier.

5. Add the weight of the sample carrier to the amount of the substance desired. Watch your significant digits!

6. Add the desired substance until you have reached the appropriate weight.

an electronic balance

Many electronic balances allow you to subtract the mass of the carrier from the total mass of the sample and carrier. If your balance has such a "tare" function, your teacher will instruct you in how to use it.

Using a Bunsen Burner

Bunsen burners are the most common source of heat in chemistry laboratories. They are popular because they give a hot flame and they burn clean, readily available natural gas. Bunsen burners work well because they mix gas with the correct amount of air to produce the most heat. If air is not mixed with the gas before it burns, not all the gas will burn, and the flame will not be as hot. If too much air is mixed with the gas, it "snuffs out" the flame.

Take your Bunsen burner apart and then reassemble it, identifying each part as you do. Connect the Bunsen burner to the desk gas line with a rubber hose, open the main gas valve, and light the burner with a match or a flint. Adjustments to the flame should be made from the needle valve and the air valves. If the burner lights but the flame immediately goes out, try reducing the gas flow at the needle valve. A yellow flame signifies that not enough air is mixing with the gas. A flame that makes a noise like a roaring wind means that too much air is entering the barrel. This extra air may cool the flame or blow it out entirely.

barrel

Air enters here.

needle valve

Gas enters here.

gas adjustment

base

Bunsen burner

outer flame

hottest point

inner blue flame

inner cone of unburned gases

proper Bunsen burner flame

smoky yellow flame spreading at the top

yellow

no inner cone

improper Bunsen burner flame

To get the best flame possible, rotate the barrel until the flame is entirely blue and two distinct zones of blue appear. Place objects to be heated at the tip of the inner blue zone for quick heating.

Sometimes the flame strikes back; that is, it enters the barrel and comes out the bottom. If this happens, do not panic. Turn off the gas supply and readjust the Bunsen burner so that not so much air enters the barrel.

The flame is yellow because small particles of unburned carbon become incandescent and glow.

Handling Liquids

Proper technique for handling liquids is essential if you are to remain safe, keep reagents pure, and obtain accurate measurements. For increased safety, do not splash or splatter liquids when pouring. Pour them slowly down the insides of test tubes and beakers. If anything is spilled, wipe it up quickly. To keep liquids from running down the outside of the container from which you are pouring, pour the liquid down a stirring rod.

In order to keep the liquid chemicals pure, keep stirring rods and spatulas out of the stock supply. Do not let the stoppers and lids become contaminated while you are pouring. Instead, hold the stopper between your fingers. If you must put a lid down, keep the inside surface from touching the surface of the table.

| right | wrong | right | wrong |

Accurate measurements of liquids can be made in burets, graduated cylinders, and volumetric flasks. You should measure volumes in these pieces of glassware unless you need only a rough approximation. When reading the level of a liquid, look at the bottom of the meniscus (curved surface) along a horizontal line of sight.

Accurately measure all amounts of solid substances.

Read the level of a liquid at the bottom of the meniscus.

Scoop out a little of the sample with the spatula.

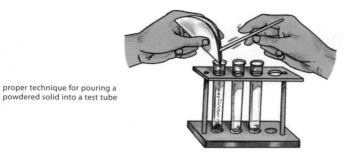

Gently tap the spatula until the
desired amount falls off.

proper technique for pouring a
powdered solid into a test tube

Using a Thermometer

Select a thermometer that has the proper temperature range for the experiment you will be doing. Support the thermometer in a one-hole rubber stopper. To avoid breaking the thermometer and cutting your hand while inserting the thermometer in the stopper, lubricate the thermometer and the stopper hole with soap or glycerol. Then protect your hands with paper towels. Hold the thermometer near the stopper and gently twist it into the hole. If you have to use a great amount of force, ask your instructor to enlarge the hole.

Position the thermometer bulb just above the bottom of the container. If the bulb touches the container, your readings will be inaccurate. If a thermometer breaks, alert your instructor and do not touch the inner contents. Some thermometers still contain mercury. The spilled mercury may look fascinating, but it is toxic and can be absorbed through the skin. Due to the health and safety factors associated with mercury as well as the expense of cleanup, the use of mercury thermometers is discouraged.

how to properly insert a thermometer
into a rubber stopper

Spilled mercury should be cleaned up using a mercury spill kit.

Separating Liquids and Solids

Several experiments require that you remove a solid from a liquid. The most common method of separation, filtering, involves passing the solution through a fine sieve such as filter paper. The paper allows the liquid and dissolved particles to pass through but catches undissolved particles.

The filter paper must be folded to fit the funnel. Fold it into two halves and then fold it again at an angle slightly less than 90° to the first fold. Tear off the corner of the last fold as shown. Open the paper to form a cone; half of the cone should have three layers of paper, and the other half should have one layer. Place the cone in a funnel and wet the paper with a few drops of distilled water to hold it in place. Seal the edge of the paper against the edge of the funnel so that none of the solution can go down the spout without going through the paper.

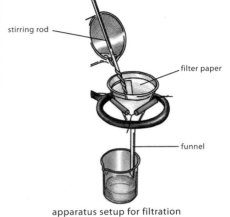

apparatus setup for filtration

Fold.

Fold again.

Open into a cone.

folding a piece of filter paper

Decanting is a quick method that is often acceptable for separating a liquid from a solid. To decant, gently pour the liquid off the top of the residue that is at the bottom of the container. Avoid causing turbulence that could mix the solid with the liquid. Sometimes the solid residue may be rinsed off with distilled water for a second decanting.

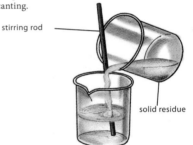

decanting a liquid from a precipitate

Appendix D
Laboratory Safety and First-Aid Rules

Safety in the Laboratory

1. **Attitude**

   a. The chemistry laboratory must only be used for serious work.

   b. Never perform any unauthorized experiment.

   c. Always report any accident, injury, or incorrect procedure to your teacher at once.

2. **Attire**

   a. Always wear safety glasses or goggles while working in the lab.

   b. Always wear a laboratory apron.

   c. Tie back long hair.

   d. Avoid wearing clothing with loose sleeves.

   e. Avoid wearing neckties.

3. **Glassware**

   a. Lubricate glass tubing and thermometers before inserting them into rubber stoppers.

   b. Place broken glass in a designated container.

4. **Handling chemicals**

   a. Read labels on reagent bottles carefully.

   b. Avoid contaminating the chemicals. Do not return unused chemicals to bottles or insert your pipet into the bottle or lay the stopper of a bottle down. If you must put a lid down, keep the inside surface from touching the surface of the table.

   c. Never taste anything unless specifically directed to do so.

   d. When smelling a substance, waft its vapor gently toward you.

   e. Always add acid to water slowly when diluting acid solutions. Never add water to an acid.

   f. Keep combustible materials away from open flames.

5. **Heating substances**

   When heating substances in a test tube, do not point the mouth of the test tube toward anyone, and keep the tube moving in the flame.

6. **Preparation**

   Study your assignment before you come to the laboratory. Make sure that you understand EVERY procedure.

7. **Safety equipment**

   Know the location of the fire extinguisher, safety shower, eyewash, fire blanket, first-aid kit, and MSDS binder.

First Aid in the Laboratory

1. **Burns**

   For burns from hot objects, flames, or chemicals, flush the area with cold water for several minutes.

2. **Chemical spills**

   a. On a laboratory desk

Hold the glass tube with a cloth near the end to be inserted and twist as you push.

Poisonous substances are not always labeled as such in the laboratory.

The reason you add acid to water is that the heat generated by pouring water into an acid may splatter the mixture or break the glass.

Demonstrate the use of and show the location of each piece of safety equipment.

To neutralize acid on clothing, use a saturated sodium hydrogen carbonate (baking soda) solution. For a base on clothing, use saturated boric acid. For an acid or base on a desk, use solid sodium hydrogen carbonate followed by water. Specific cautions for certain chemicals will accompany the lab in which they are used.

    1. If the material is not particularly volatile, toxic, or flammable, use an absorbent material that will neutralize the liquid. Then clean the area with soap and water.

    2. If the material is volatile, flammable, or toxic, extinguish all flames and evacuate the lab.

    3. When materials such as mercury, alkali metals, white phosphorus, or hydrochloric acid are spilled, the teacher will clean them up.

  b. On a person

    1. If it is a large area, remove all contaminated clothing while under the safety shower. Flood the affected body area for fifteen minutes. Obtain medical help immediately.

    2. If it is a small area, immediately flush the affected area with cold water for several minutes. Then wash the area with a mild detergent solution.

    3. If it is an acid, rinse the area with sodium bicarbonate solution; if it is a base, use boric acid solution.

    4. If the chemical splashes in the eyes, immediately wash the eyes in the nearest eyewash fountain for several minutes. Get medical attention.

3. **Fire**

  a. Smother a small fire with a cloth or beaker.

  b. Use a fire extinguisher for a larger fire.

  c. If a person's clothes are on fire, roll the person on the floor and use a fire blanket to extinguish the flames. The safety shower may also be used. DO NOT use a fire extinguisher.

4. **Swallowing chemicals**

Find out the specific substance ingested. Contact the Poison Control Center in your area immediately.

To the Teacher

The Teacher's Edition of CHEMISTRY: *Laboratory Manual,* Third Edition consists of the student manual on reduced student pages with overprint answers and summary charts to aid you in planning laboratory activities. This Teacher's Edition contains helpful comments in the margins placed as close as possible to where they are needed. Any necessary notes for the materials are placed at the top of the side column. The summary charts here in the back are used to determine the extent to which materials are used and sources for supplies and information. The list of science suppliers has been updated from the second edition. All of these companies have websites for ordering. There is also a table entitled *Local Sources for Common Chemicals* that provides alternatives as well as sources for the procurement of many common lab chemicals. These tips are especially helpful for homeschoolers and small Christian schools that need only small amounts of certain chemicals.

The student laboratory manual contains thirty-five experiments designed to accompany the text, CHEMISTRY, Third Edition, and to cover all aspects of the definition of problem-solving tasks. Problem-solving tasks embody planning and designing, performance, analysis and interpretation, and application. In addition to the laboratory exercises in this manual, the CD that accompanies the Teacher's Edition of CHEMISTRY, Third Edition contains five lab exercises that are more open and allow students to demonstrate the inductive processes of science by arriving at an answer to a question. The structured experiments of this lab manual are of a typical high-school style, but the unstructured experiments on the CD allow students to invent and test a procedure. It is suggested that you use several of these optional CD labs throughout the year in place of the ones that are in this lab manual. Although to some students this open approach may be frustrating and time consuming, there are several advantages: (1) The students learn quickly that they must come to the laboratory well prepared, or they will accomplish nothing. (2) Thinking is a must! (3) It is a more realistic approach because it is the approach that scientists use. (4) Writing skills are emphasized since students must write their own laboratory reports.

Most states have requirements for the minimum amount of laboratory time in order for credit to be given for an upper-level science course. It is typically 20% of total class time, but demonstrations and other hands-on experiences can count toward the total. The suggested teaching schedules in the Teacher's Edition of CHEMISTRY, Third Edition take this into consideration. For a typical chapter, one lab is suggested. Longer chapters may include two labs. In some cases, additional alternate labs are provided.

An awareness of several items will help the students to perform better in the laboratory. (1) Whenever the students are told to determine the mass, they should always do so to 0.01 g. (2) The students should keep distilled water in their water bottles to use whenever they make up a solution or use water in a reaction. (3) The students should keep the graded laboratory sheets in a notebook for quick reference. (4) Since the procedures alone will usually take fifty minutes, the students need to be prepared. That is why the assignments in the textbook Teacher's Edition call for students to review the lab and answer the Checkup questions in advance. Each lab is designed to be completed in a typical class period of 45–50 minutes. This time should be adequate for completing the Procedure and Data sections, but not necessarily for answering all of the Analysis questions.

You should read the laboratory experiment at least one week before you plan to use it. (You will need to make up some solutions several days in advance.) Use the following chart to help you determine when to use each laboratory exercise.

Lab Number	Lab Sequence with Text	Lab Number	Lab Sequence with Text
1	after Section 1C	11	with Section 10B
2A	after Section 2A	11 (alt) (on CD)	with Section 11C, after Subsection 11.18
2B	with Section 2B	12A	after Section 12A
2B (alt)	with Section 2B	12B	after Section 12C
2C (on CD)	with Section 2B	13A	with Section 13A
3A	after Section 3C	13B	with Section 13A, after Subsection 13.4
3B	after Section 3D	13C	after Section 13A
3C (on CD)	after Section 3D	14	after Section 14A
4A	after Section 4A	15	after Section 15A
4B	with Section 4C	15 (alt) (on CD)	after Section 15A
5	after Section 5B	16A	after Section 16B
6	after Section 6C	16A (alt)	after Section 16B
7	after Section 7B	16B	with Section 16C, after Subsection 16.15
8	after Section 8D	17A	after Section 17A
9A	after Section 9A	17B	after Section 17A
9B	after Section 9A	18A	after Section 18C
9C	after Section 9A	18B	with Section 18D
9D (on CD)	with Section 9A, after Subsection 9.5	18C	with Section 18E, after Subsection 18.24
10A	after Section 10B	19	after Section 19B
10B	after Section 10C	20	with Section 20B, after Subsection 20.16

Sources of Scientific Supplies

American Education Products, LLC
401 Hickory Street
PO Box 2121
Ft. Collins, CO 80522
1-800-289-9299
www.amep.com

Carolina Biological Supply Company
PO Box 6010
Burlington, NC 27216-6010
(800) 334-5551
www.carolina.com

Fisher Scientific
2000 Park Lane Drive
Pittsburgh, PA 15275
(800) 766-7000
www.fishersci.com

Flinn Scientific, Inc.
PO Box 219
Batavia, IL 60510
1-800-452-1261
www.flinnsci.com

Frey Scientific
80 Northwest Blvd.
Nashua, NH 03603
1-800-225-3739
www.freyscientific.com

Lab Safety Supply, Inc.
PO Box 1368
Janesville, WI 53547-1368
(800) 356-0783
www.labsafety.com

Nasco
PO Box 901
901 Janesville Ave.
Fort Atkinson, WI 53538-0901
1-800-558-9595
www.enasco.com

Ohaus Scale Corporation
19A Chapin Road
PO Box 2033
Pine Brook, NJ 07058
(800) 672-7722
www.ohaus.com

Sargent-Welch Scientific Company
PO Box 4130
Buffalo, NY 14217
(800) 727-4368
www.sargentwelch.com

Thomas Scientific
PO Box 99
Swedesboro, NJ 08085
(800) 345-2100
www.thomassci.com

Ward's Natural Science
5100 West Henrietta Road
PO Box 92912
Rochester, NY 14692-9012
(800) 962-2660
www.wardsci.com

Local Sources for Common Chemicals

Many chemicals used in science classrooms are common household chemicals. Knowing the common names of these chemicals can save you a great deal of money because you can use the common chemical instead of ordering the pure grade from a science supplier. Notwithstanding, it may be well to remember that while these items will be less expensive and more readily available, they may not have the same purity as chemicals purchased from suppliers. In nearly all cases, however, household chemicals will suffice for classroom work.

This list contains some items that are not used in this laboratory manual. The extra items are included because they are occasionally used in experiments that you may find in other books, encyclopedias, or magazines that are commonly used as supplementary materials.

Name of Chemical	Alternative
acetic acid	White vinegar is 0.5% acetic acid (1 M). It can be purchased from a grocery store.
acetone	Some nail polish removers are mostly acetone and will work for most experiments. Some hardware stores carry acetone as a paint thinner.
agar	Use unflavored gelatin. The concentration will need to be increased.
aluminum	Many everyday objects (aluminum nails, soft drink cans, etc.) are made of aluminum. Find an inexpensive piece. Cut, grind, or file it; collect the filings to fit your needs.
ammonium hydroxide	Ammonia (a household cleaner) is a 28% aqueous solution of ammonium hydroxide (15 M). Make a 1 M solution from 50 mL of cleaner per 1000 mL of water or 5 mL of cleaner per 100 mL of water. Use a brand that does not have fragrance or detergents added.
boric acid	Boric acid in solution is used as an eyewash and is available from drugstores. It is also used in powdered roach killer. Check the labels carefully.
calcium carbonate	White chalk, marble chips, eggshells, and seashells are all calcium carbonate.
calcium chloride	Some sidewalk deicing salts are pelletized calcium chloride. It is also sold as a calcium hardness increaser at swimming pool supply stores. This chemical is also found in most chemistry sets.
calcium hydroxide	Hydrated lime, sometimes called *slaked lime*, is calcium hydroxide. It is available from hardware and garden supply stores.
calcium hypochlorite	This is the common "chlorine" additive for swimming pools. Check at a swimming pool supply store.
calcium oxide	This is also called *quicklime* or *dehydrated lime*. It is available from garden supply stores, chemistry sets, and hobby shops.
calcium sulfate	Plaster of Paris, or gypsum, is calcium sulfate. It is available from hardware and building supply stores.
charcoal powder	Aquarium charcoal ground to a powder is the same thing.
copper (sheets, shavings, wires)	Copper is available in many forms. Copper nails and copper plumbing fittings are easily obtainable and can be hammered into thin sheets and cut into strips. Cutting a piece with a hacksaw will produce copper filings. Copper wiring is readily available from hardware and building supply stores.
cupric sulfate	This is commonly called *Bluestone* or *copper (II) sulfate*. It is usually used in the pentahydrate form ($CuSO_4 \cdot 5H_2O$). It is available from hardware stores, garden supply stores, and some hobby shops.
dextrose (glucose)	This is available from some grocery stores and most pharmacies.
distilled water	This is available at most grocery stores. Be careful not to get mineral water. Distilled water is not boiled water, but rather condensed steam.
dry ice	Dry ice is available in most grocery stores. It is usually in a chest freezer, cut into chunks of various sizes and wrapped in paper. You should transport it in a cooler and keep it in a freezer until use.

Name of Chemical	Alternative
ethanol, denatured	This is used as a solvent and is usually called *denatured alcohol* or *ethyl alcohol*. It is available from paint and hardware stores.
glycerin	This is also called *glycerol*. It is available at most pharmacies.
hydrochloric acid	Hydrochloric acid, also called *muriatic acid*, is found in hardware and building supply stores. It is also available in some farm supply stores. It is used for cleaning concrete. (Muriatic acid is about 6 M. Concentrated acid from a science supplier is 12 M.) For dilute acid, add 17 mL of muriatic acid to 83 mL of distilled water to make 100 mL of 1 M solution.
hydrogen peroxide	A 3% hydrogen peroxide solution is used for medicinal purposes (available from most stores); 10% is used for bleaching hair. (Check with a hair salon.) A 3% solution will work for most experiments.
iron filings	Cut an iron concrete nail with a hacksaw and collect the filings. Fine steel wool will also work. Auto repair and machine shops may also be a good source.
iron (II) sulfate	Iron (II) sulfate is available from some hobby shops.
iron (II) sulfide	You can make your own by mixing 1 part iron filings with 2 parts sulfur. Burn in a crucible over a hot flame. The remaining solid is iron (II) sulfide.
iron (III) chloride	This is also called *ferric chloride* and is available from some hobby shops.
kerosene	Use vegetable oil. Kerosene is available at some gas stations or in cans at sporting goods stores.
lard	Any form of animal fat will work.
lead shot	The smallest split-shot fishing sinkers make a good substitute.
lead sulfide	Galena, found in rock shops and hobby stores, is essentially lead sulfide. If you have a commercially purchased rock collection, it probably has a galena sample. It will be pure enough for most experiments.
lithium chloride	Lithium chloride is available from most hobby shops.
magnesium (metal)	Magnesium can be found in fire starters (camping supplies). Old flashbulbs also use magnesium filaments. If you can find them, two or three bulbs will contain enough magnesium for most experiments.
magnesium chloride	Magnesium chloride is available from most hobby shops.
magnesium dioxide	This can be obtained from some hobby shops. The black powder in a dry cell (flashlight battery) will also work. (Wear gloves when cutting open the battery.) It is used as a catalyst in many reactions, especially for releasing oxygen from hydrogen peroxide or from potassium chlorate. Although some acid is found on the powder, it is not significant enough to affect the reaction.
magnesium hydroxide	Milk of magnesia is magnesium hydroxide.
magnesium silicate	Talcum powder is magnesium silicate.
magnesium sulfate	Epsom salt is magnesium sulfate. It is available at drugstores and grocery stores.
methanol	Methanol is commonly sold as wood alcohol. It is used as a weed killer and is often sold in hardware and farm supply stores.
methyl orange indicator	This is available from swimming pool supply stores.
methyl red indicator	This is available from swimming pool supply stores. It is one of the solutions used in pH test kits.
petroleum ether	Many brands of charcoal lighter fluid and engine additives are petroleum ether (also called *petroleum distillates*); e.g., fuel injector and carburetor cleaners, engine cleaners, and fuel additives. Check the labels for contents.

Name of Chemical	Alternative
phenol red	Phenol red is commonly used as an acid-base indicator for swimming pools. Check your local swimming pool supply store.
potassium bitartrate	This is also called *potassium hydrogen tartrate*, or *cream of tartar*. This is available at a grocery store in the spice aisle.
potassium chloride	No-sodium salt substitutes are 5% potassium chloride. It is often available in its pure form from a hobby shop.
potassium hydroxide	Some drain cleaners are potassium hydroxide. Check the labels.
potassium nitrate	Potassium nitrate, also called *saltpeter* or *niter*, is available from some drugstores and hobby shops. It is sold at hardware stores and plant nurseries for stump removal.
potassium sodium tartrate	Rochelle salt, a compound used as a laxative and in silvering mirrors, is potassium sodium tartrate. It is available at some drugstores and hobby shops.
sodium bicarbonate	Baking soda is sodium bicarbonate. It is also called *sodium hydrogen carbonate*. It is available at grocery stores.
sodium bisulfate	Sodium bisulfate is sold at swimming pool supply stores. It is also called *pH down*.
sodium carbonate	Sodium carbonate is called *washing soda* or *soda ash*. It is available from some grocery stores and most swimming pool supply stores. It is often called *pH up*.
sodium chloride	Table salt is almost pure sodium chloride. Non-iodized salt is pure sodium chloride. Either is acceptable for high-school science experiments.
sodium hydroxide	This is called *caustic soda*, or *lye*. It is found at hardware and grocery stores. Some drain cleaners contain both sodium hydroxide and potassium hydroxide. Crystalline Drano® is 99% sodium hydroxide.
sodium hypochlorite	Ordinary bleach is sodium hypochlorite. It is available from most stores.
sodium tetraborate	Borax powder is sodium tetraborate. It is available at grocery stores.
sodium thiosulfate	The "hypo agent" (fixing agent) used in photographic development is sodium thiosulfate. It is available from a photo supply store.
stearic acid	Stearic acid is available from some hobby shops.
strontium chloride	Strontium chloride is available from some hobby shops.
sucrose	Table sugar is sucrose. It is available at grocery stores.
sulfur	Sulfur is available at most drugstores and hobby shops.
sulfuric acid	Battery acid and some commercial drain cleaners contain sulfuric acid. (18 M; for dilute acid, add 6 mL of concentrated acid to 94 mL of distilled water for 100 mL of 2 M solution.) It is available but may be difficult to obtain from professional plumbing suppliers.
thymol blue	Thymol blue is available from swimming pool supply stores.
zinc	Metal casing of some used flashlight batteries can be used for zinc. Alkaline batteries use steel cases rather than zinc. Test the case with a magnet. Zinc is nonmagnetic, whereas steel or iron is magnetic. Zinc is also available from hobby shops.

Chemicals Frequency Chart	1	2A	2B	2B (alt)	3A	3B	4A	4B	5	6	7	8	9A	9B	9C	10A	10B	11
acetic acid																		
acetone										•								
agar																		
ammonia solution			•															
ammonium chloride																		
antifreeze (ethylene glycol)																		
Benedict's reagent																		
boric acid												•						
calcium chloride							•											
celery																		
chlorine bleach																		
copper (II) chloride							•											
copper (II) sulfate pentahydrate														•				
copper wire																		
copper wool												•						
corn oil																		
ethyl alcohol																		
gelatin																		
glucose																		
hydrochloric acid				•												•		
ice cubes																•		•
iodine		•																
iron (II) sulfide				•														
iron (III) chloride																		
iron (III) oxide																	•	
iron filings		•		•						•								
iron nails																		
isopropyl alcohol solution																		
lard																		
lithium chloride							•											
litmus paper, blue																		
litmus paper, red																		
magnesium chloride																		
magnesium ribbon													•					
metal shot (zinc or copper)						•												
methyl alcohol																		
methyl orange																		
methyl red																		
milk																		
mineral oil																		
p-dichlorobenzene (mothball crystals)										•								
pH paper (opt.)																		
phenolphthalein																		
potassium chlorate																	•	
potassium chloride							•											
potassium ferricyanide																		
potassium hydrogen phthalate																		
potassium iodide																		
potassium nitrate																		
potassium thiocyanate																		
red cabbage extract																		
sand		•																
sodium carbonate			•															
sodium chloride		•					•			•								
sodium hydrogen carbonate (sodium bicarbonate)			•									•			•			
sodium hydroxide												•						
sodium thiosulfate			•															
starch																		
strontium chloride							•											
sulfur				•														
sulfuric acid												•						
synthetic detergent																		
t-butyl alcohol																		
thymol blue																		
tin strip																		
vegetable oil																	•	
vinegar																		
zinc strip																		

Chemicals Frequency Chart	12A	12B	13A	13B	13C	14	15	16A	16A (alt)	16B	17A	17B	18A	18B	18C	19	20
acetic acid								•	•		•						
acetone															•		
agar												•					
ammonia solution																	
ammonium chloride	•																
antifreeze (ethylene glycol)		•															
Benedict's reagent															•		
boric acid								•									
calcium chloride														•			
celery		•															
chlorine bleach											•						
copper (II) chloride																	
copper (II) sulfate pentahydrate															•		
copper wire		•										•				•	
copper wool																	
corn oil																•	
ethyl alcohol		•												•			
gelatin															•		
glucose															•		
hydrochloric acid					•	•		•	•					•			
ice cubes		•	•			•								•			
iodine															•		
iron (II) sulfide																	
iron (III) chloride							•							•			
iron (III) oxide																	
iron filings																	
iron nails												•					
isopropyl alcohol solution																•	
lard														•			
lithium chloride																	
litmus paper, blue								•									
litmus paper, red								•									
magnesium chloride														•			
magnesium ribbon					•												
metal shot (zinc or copper)				•													
methyl alcohol		•															
methyl orange									•								
methyl red									•								
milk															•		
mineral oil														•			
p-dichlorobenzene (mothball crystals)																	
pH paper (opt.)								•									
phenolphthalein										•		•		•			
potassium chlorate																	
potassium chloride							•										
potassium ferricyanide												•					
potassium hydrogen phthalate								•		•							
potassium iodide												•			•		
potassium nitrate					•												
potassium thiocyanate							•										
red cabbage extract								•									
sand																	
sodium carbonate								•									
sodium chloride		•						•				•		•		•	
sodium hydrogen carbonate (sodium bicarbonate)					•	•		•									
sodium hydroxide					•			•		•				•	•		
sodium thiosulfate						•					•						
starch											•				•		
strontium chloride																	
sulfur																	
sulfuric acid																	
synthetic detergent														•			
t-butyl alcohol		•															
thymol blue									•								
tin strip												•					
vegetable oil															•		
vinegar									•								
zinc strip												•					

Chemicals for Experiments

Chemical	Source*	Lab	Notes
acetic acid (CH_3COOH)	S	16A	0.1 M; 2 mL per group (Dilute 10 mL of 1 M acetic acid to 100 mL.)
		16A (alt)	0.1 M; 10 mL per group 1 M; 10 mL per group (1 M acetic acid is 6% acetic acid; glacial acetic acid is 17.4 M.) (Dilute 6 mL of glacial acetic acid to 1000 mL in a graduated cylinder or volumetric flask, using distilled water.)
		17A	glacial; 60 mL per group
acetone (CH_3COCH_3)	L or S	6	10 mL per group
		18C	5 mL per group
agar	S	17B	0.5 g per group
ammonia solution (NH_3)	S	2B	6 M; 3 drops per group (Dilute 40 mL of stock 15 M to 100 mL.)
ammonium chloride (NH_4Cl)	S	12A	19 g per group
antifreeze (ethylene glycol)	L	12B	0.3 mL per group
Benedict's reagent	S	18C	20 mL per group
boric acid (H_3BO_3)	L or S	8	saturated solution (This is also used as first aid for base contact and as an emergency eyewash in many labs.)
		16A	saturated solution
calcium chloride ($CaCl_2$)	S	4A	0.5 g per group
		18B	0.1 M; 10 drops per group (Dissolve 11.2 g $CaCl_2$ per L of solution.)
celery	L	12B	2 1-inch pieces per group
chlorine bleach	L	17A	12 mL per group
copper (II) chloride ($CuCl_2$)	S	4A	0.5 g per group
copper (II) sulfate pentahydrate ($CuSO_4 \cdot 5H_2O$)	S	9B	2–3 g per group
		18C	2%; 12 drops per group
copper wire	L or S	12B	1 25-centimeter piece per group
		17B	1 15-centimeter piece per group
		19	1 5-inch piece per group (An 18-gauge wire works well.)
copper wool	S	8	1 g per group
corn oil	L	19	It may be possible to substitute another vegetable oil, but see note in lab first.
ethyl alcohol (C_2H_5OH)	L or S	12B	0.4 mL per group
		18B	10 mL per group
gelatin	L	18C	1%; 1 mL per group (See instructions in lab.)
glucose (dextrose, $C_6H_{12}O_6$)	L or S	18C	1%; 1 mL per group
hydrochloric acid (HCl)	L or S	2B (alt)	6 M; 10 mL per group (Dilute 500 mL of stock 12 M HCl to 1 L.)

Chemical	Source*	Lab	Notes
		9C	6 *M*; 6 mL per group
		13C	1.00 *M*; 125 mL per group (Dilute 83.3 mL stock acid to 1 L.)
		14	1.0 *M*; 40 mL per group
		16A	0.1 *M*; 2 mL per group (Dilute 10 mL of 1.0 *M* to 100 mL.)
		16A (alt)	0.1 *M*; 15 mL per group
		18B	6 *M*; 10 mL per group
ice cubes	L	10A	1 tray per group
		11	1 tray per group (crushed)
		12B	1 tray per group (crushed)
		13A	1 tray per group
		14	1 tray per group
		18B	1 tray per group
iodine (I_2)	S	2B	0.3 g per group
		18C	9 drops iodine solution per group (See instructions in lab.)
iron (II) sulfide (FeS)	S	2B (alt)	1–3 g per group
iron (III) chloride ($FeCl_3$)	S	15	0.25 *M*; 3 mL per group (Dissolve 40.6 g $FeCl_3$ per L of solution.)
		18B	0.1 *M*; 10 drops per group (Dissolve 16.2 g $FeCl_3$ per L of solution.)
iron (III) oxide (Fe_2O_3)	S	10B	0.1 g per group
iron filings (Fe)	S	2B	0.5 g per group
		2B (alt)	3–5 g per group
		6	0.5 g per group
iron nails (6d)	L	17B	4 per group
isopropyl alcohol solution (C_3H_8O)	L	19	45% solution (Dilute 45.5 mL of pure isopropyl alcohol or propan-2-ol with 100 mL of deionized water, or dilute 65.0 mL of 70% isopropyl alcohol with 100 mL of water.)
lard	L	18B	10 g per group
lithium chloride (LiCl)	S	4A	0.5 g per group
litmus paper, blue	S	16A	8 strips per group
litmus paper, red	S	16A	8 strips per group
magnesium chloride ($MgCl_2$)	S	18B	0.1 *M*; 10 drops per group (Dissolve 13.1 g $MgCl_2$ per L of solution.)
magnesium ribbon (Mg)	S	9A	0.2–0.3 g per group (25–30 cm piece)
		13C	0.10–0.15 g per group (11–16 cm piece)
metal shot (Zn or Cu)	S	3B	30 g per group

Chemical	Source*	Lab	Notes
		13B	50–70 g per group
methyl alcohol (CH_3OH)	L or S	12B	0.2 mL per group
methyl orange	S	16A (alt)	21 drops per group (0.01%)
methyl red	S	16A (alt)	21 drops per group (0.02%)
milk	L	18C	3 mL per group
mineral oil	L	18B	30 drops per group
p-dichlorobenzene (mothball crystals)	L or S	6	0.5 g per group
pH paper, pH 0–13 (opt.)	S	16A	1 18-centimeter strip per group
phenolphthalein	S	16B	0.5%; 1 mL per group (Dissolve 0.5 g phenolphthalein in 50 mL ethanol; dilute to 100 mL with distilled water.)
		17B	2 mL per group
		18B	5–10 drops per group
potassium chlorate ($KClO_3$)	S	10B	1 g per group
potassium chloride (KCl)	S	4A	0.5 g per group
		15	1 g per group
potassium ferricyanide ($K_3Fe[CN]_6$)	S	17B	0.1 M; 1 mL per group (Dissolve 32.9 g $K_3[Fe(CN)_6]$ per L of solution.)
potassium hydrogen phthalate ($KHC_8H_4O_4$, or KHP)	S	16A	0.1 g per group
		16B	2 g per group
potassium iodide (KI)	S	17A	21 g per group
		18C	2 g per 100 mL iodine solution
potassium nitrate (KNO_3)	S	13C	3–4 g per group
potassium thiocyanate (KSCN)	S	15	0.25 M; 3 mL per group (Dissolve 24.3 g KSCN per L of solution.)
red cabbage extract	L	16A	1 leaf boiled in distilled water
sand	L	2A	2 g per group (includes the salt in the mixture)
sodium carbonate (Na_2CO_3)	S	2B (alt)	3 g per group for waste treatment
		16A	0.1 g per group
sodium chloride (NaCl)	L or S	2A	2 g per group (includes the sand in the mixture)
		4A	0.5 g per group
		6	0.5 g per group
		12B	75 mL per group (Dissolve 36 g NaCl per 100 mL of H_2O.)
		16A	0.1 g per group
		17B	5 g per group

Chemical	Source*	Lab	Notes
		18B	18 g per group
		19	40 mL per group (Dissolve 36 g NaCl per 100 mL of H_2O.)
sodium hydrogen carbonate (sodium bicarbonate, $NaHCO_3$)	L or S	2B (alt)	saturated solution, used for first aid in acid contact
		8	saturated solution, first aid
		9C	3 g per group
		13C	saturated solution, first aid
		14	saturated solution, first aid
		16A	saturated solution, first aid
sodium hydroxide (lye, NaOH)	L or S	8	6 M; 10 mL per group (Cautiously dissolve 240 g NaOH per L of solution while stirring.)
		13C	1 M; 35 mL per group (Dissolve 40 g NaOH per L of solution.)
		16A	0.1 M; 2 mL per group (Dissolve 4 g NaOH per L of solution, or dilute 10 mL of 1 M NaOH to 100 mL.)
		16B	approx. 0.1 M; 100 mL per group
		18B	6 M; 15 mL per group
		18C	6 M; 20 drops per group
sodium thiosulfate (hypo, $Na_2S_2O_3$)	L or S	2B	solution used for I_2 stains
		14	0.10 M; 30 mL per group plus 55 mL for teacher (Dissolve 15.81 g $Na_2S_2O_3$ per L of solution.)
		17A	0.100 M; 160 mL per group
starch	L or S	17A	0.5%; 12 mL per group (See instructions in Lab 18C.)
		18C	1%; 1 mL per group (See instructions in lab.)
strontium chloride (SrCl)	S	4A	0.5 g per group
sulfur (S)	S	2B (alt)	3–5 g per group
sulfuric acid (H_2SO_4)	L or S	8	6 M; 5 mL per group (Cautiously dilute 333 mL of stock 18 M acid to 1 L while cooling.)
synthetic detergent	L	18B	3 g per group
t-butyl alcohol	S	12B	13–20 mL per group
thymol blue	S	16A (alt)	21 drops per group (Dissolve 0.1 g in 21.6 mL of 0.01 M NaOH; dilute to 125 mL with distilled water. Prepare 0.01 M NaOH by diluting 5 mL of 0.1 M NaOH to 50 mL.)
tin strip (Sn)	S	17B	1 5-centimeter piece per group
vegetable oil	L	10A	1 mL per group
		18C	1 drop per group
vinegar	L	16B	35 mL per group (Two or more brands may be needed.)
zinc strip (Zn)	S	17B	1 5-centimeter piece per group

Equipment Frequency Chart

Equipment Frequency Chart	1	2A	2B	2B alt	3A	3B	4A	4B	5	6	7	8	9A	9B	9C	10A	10B
balance		•	•		•	•		•		•			•	•	•		•
barometer																	•
beaker (150 mL)	•	•										•			•		•
beaker (250 mL)	•	•										•					•
beaker (400 mL)																	
beaker (600 mL)																•	
beaker (1000 mL)																	
boiling stones																	
Bunsen burner	•	•	•	•			•			•		•	•	•	•	•	•
buret																	
buret clamp																	
cardboard																	
clay											•						
clay triangle	•	•										•	•	•			
colored pencils (optional)							•										
conductivity tester										•							
cork																	
crucible and cover	•											•	•	•			
crucible tongs	•	•										•	•	•	•	•	
diffraction grating spectroscope							•										
Erlenmeyer flask (250 mL)	•																•
evaporating dish	•	•	•							•					•		
filtering funnel (3–4")	•	•										•					
filter paper	•	•										•					
forceps (optional)																	
glass stirring rod	•		•									•				•	
goggles	•	•	•	•			•			•		•					
graduated cylinder (10 mL)	•	•	•	•	•	•						•					
graduated cylinder (25 mL)												•					
graduated cylinder (100 mL)																	•
incandescent light							•										
iron ring	•	•	•							•		•	•	•	•	•	
laboratory apron	•	•	•	•			•			•		•	•	•	•	•	•
M&M's, plain and peanut (or comparable)								•									
magnet			•	•													
magnifying glass			•														
marker, black																	
matches	•	•	•	•			•			•		•	•	•	•	•	•
melting point capillary tubes, ≥10 cm																•	
metal bar or cylinder					•												
metric ruler					•	•			•							•	
mortar and pestle																	
pennies					•												
pH meter (optional)																	
pH paper (optional)																	
pinchcock clamp	•																•
plastic wrap																	
polystyrene cups (6–8 oz)																	
reference source																	
ring stand	•	•	•									•	•	•	•	•	•
rubber bands, orthodontic																•	
rubber stopper																	•
sandpaper (100–200 grit)														•			
spatula	•		•												•		
test tube brush	•		•	•	•					•					•		
test tube clamp	•															•	•
test tube holder	•		•														
test tube, large (≥18 × 150 mm)	•																•
test tube rack	•		•	•						•							
test tubes	•		•	•	•					•					•		
thermometer																•	•
toothpicks											•						
towels, paper or cloth														•			
transfer pipets, plastic (or eyedroppers)	•		•										•		•		
tubing, glass																	•
tubing, rubber																	•
wash bottle	•														•		
watch glass, 60 mm	•																
watch glass, 150 mm	•	•													•	•	
watch with second hand																	
weighing paper			•	•						•					•		
wire gauze	•	•	•							•					•	•	
wooden splints							•										

Equipment Frequency Chart	11	12A	12B	13A	13B	13C	14	15	16A	16A alt	16B	17A	17B	18A	18B	18C	19	20
balance	•	•	•		•	•					•	•	•		•	•		
barometer																		
beaker (150 mL)			•				•	•	•		•	•			•	•	•	
beaker (250 mL)		•	•	•	•		•	•					•		•	•		
beaker (400 mL)					•													
beaker (600 mL)																		
beaker (1000 mL)	•		•															
boiling stones															•			
Bunsen burner	•	•		•	•			•	•						•	•	•	
buret							•				•	•						
buret clamp							•				•	•						
cardboard					•	•												
clay														•				
clay triangle																		
colored pencils (optional)																		
conductivity tester																		
cork																	•	
crucible and cover																		
crucible tongs													•				•	
diffraction grating spectroscope																		
Erlenmeyer flask (250 mL)								•			•	•						
evaporating dish																		
filtering funnel (3–4")											•	•						
filter paper																•		
forceps (optional)				•														
glass stirring rod		•	•						•				•		•			
goggles	•	•	•	•	•	•	•	•	•	•	•	•	•		•	•		
graduated cylinder (10 mL)		•									•		•					
graduated cylinder (25 mL)																		
graduated cylinder (100 mL)	•			•	•	•					•		•					
incandescent light																		
iron ring	•	•		•	•										•	•		
laboratory apron	•	•	•		•	•	•	•	•	•	•	•			•	•		
M&M's, plain and peanut (or comparable)																		
magnet																		
magnifying glass																		
marker, black							•				•						•	
matches	•	•		•	•			•	•						•	•		
melting point capillary tubes, ≥10 cm																		
metal bar or cylinder																		
metric ruler		•																
mortar and pestle																•		
pennies																		
pH meter (optional)									•									
pH paper (optional)									•									
pinchcock clamp																		
plastic wrap	•				•													
polystyrene cups (6–8 oz)				•	•	•												
reference source																		•
ring stand	•	•		•	•	•	•		•		•	•			•	•		
rubber bands, orthodontic																		
rubber stopper			•		•			•							•			
sandpaper (100–200 grit)						•							•					
spatula																		
test tube brush		•	•		•				•	•					•	•	•	
test tube clamp					•													
test tube holder		•			•			•										
test tube, large (≥18 × 150 mm)					•													
test tube rack							•	•	•	•					•	•		
test tubes		•	•				•	•	•	•					•	•	•	
thermometer	•	•	•	•	•	•												
toothpicks														•				
towels, paper or cloth				•		•							•					
transfer pipets, plastic (or eyedroppers)									•	•	•	•			•	•		
tubing, glass																		
tubing, rubber																		
wash bottle												•						
watch glass, 60 mm																		
watch glass, 150 mm									•									
watch with second hand						•												
weighing paper						•												
wire gauze	•	•		•	•				•						•	•		
wooden splints																		

Equipment for Experiments

*S = Supplier; L = Local

Equipment	Source*	Lab	Notes
balance	S	2A	2 per 15 students
		2B	2 per 15 students
		3A	2 per 15 students
		3B	2 per 15 students
		4B	2 per 15 students
		6	2 per 15 students
		9A	2 per 15 students
		9B	2 per 15 students
		9C	2 per 15 students
		10B	2 per 15 students
		11	2 per 15 students
		12A	2 per 15 students
		12B	2 per 15 students
		13B	2 per 15 students
		13C	2 per 15 students
		16B	2 per 15 students
		17A	2 per 15 students
		17B	2 per 15 students
		18B	2 per 15 students
		18C	2 per 15 students
barometer	S	10B	1 per teacher
beaker (150 mL)	S	1	1 per group
		2A	1 per group
		8	1 per group
		9C	1 per group
		12B	2 per group
		14	1 per group
		15	1 per group
		16A	2 per group
		16B	2 per group
		17A	1 per group
		18B	1 per group
		18C	2 per group
		19	1 per group
beaker (250 mL)	S	1	1 per group
		2A	1 per group
		8	1 per group
		10B	1 per group
		12A	1 per group
		12B	1 per group
		13A	1 per group
		13B	1 per group
		14	1 per group
		15	1 per group
		17B	1 per group
		18B	1 per group
		18C	1 per group
beaker (400 mL)	S	13B	1 per group
beaker (600 mL)	S	10A	1 per group
beaker (1000 mL)	S	11	1 per group
		12B	1 per group
boiling stones	S	18C	2–3 per group
Bunsen burner	S	1	1 per group
		2A	1 per group
		2B	1 per group
		2B (alt)	1 per group
		4A	1 per group
		6	1 per group
		8	1 per group
		9A	1 per group
		9B	1 per group
		9C	1 per group
		10A	1 per group
		10B	1 per group
		11	1 per group
		12A	1 per group
		13A	1 per group
		13B	1 per group
		15	1 per group
		16A	1 per group
		18B	1 per group
		18C	1 per group
		19	1 per group
buret	S	14	2 per group
		16B	2 per group
		17A	1 per group plus 1 per class
buret clamp	S	14	1 per group
		16B	1 per group
		17A	1 per group plus 1 per class
cardboard	L	13B	1 4-inch square per group
		13C	1 4-inch square per group
clay	L	7	1 4-ounce block per group (or 10 foam balls or 1 model kit per group)
		18A	2 4-ounce blocks per group (or 30 foam balls or 1 model kit per group)
clay triangle	S	1	1 per group
		2A	1 per group
		8	1 per group
		9A	1 per group
		9B	1 per group
colored pencils (optional)	L	4A	1 package per group (must include EM spectrum colors)
conductivity tester	L	6	1 per group
cork	L	19	1 per group
crucible and cover	S	1	1 per group
		8	1 per group
		9A	1 per group
		9B	1 per group
crucible tongs	S	1	1 per group
		2A	1 per group
		8	1 per group
		9A	1 per group
		9B	1 per group
		9C	1 per group
		10A	1 per group
		17B	1 per group
		19	1 per group
diffraction grating spectroscope	S	4A	1 per group
Erlenmeyer flask (250 mL)	S	1	1 per group
		10B	1 per group
		15	1 per group
		16B	1 per group
		17A	1 per group
evaporating dish	S	1	1 per group
		2A	1 per group

Equipment	Source*	Lab	Notes
		2B	1 per group
		6	1 per group
		9C	1 per group
filtering funnel, 3–4"	S	1	1 per group
		2A	1 per group
		8	1 per group
		16B	1 per group
		17A	1 per group
filter paper	S	1	1 package per group
		2A	1–2 per group
		8	1–2 per group
		18C	1–2 per group
forceps (optional)	S	13A	1 per group
glass stirring rod	S	1	1 per group
		2B	1 per group
		8	1 per group
		10A	1 per group
		12A	1 per group
		12B	1 per group
		16A	1 per group
		17B	1 per group
		18B	1 per group
goggles	S	most	1 per person
graduated cylinder (10 mL)	S	1	1 per group
		2A	1 per group
		2B	1 per group
		2B (alt)	1 per group
		3A	1 per group
		3B	1 per group
		8	1 per group
		12A	1 per group
		14	1 per group
		16A (alt)	1 per group
		17A	1 per group
		18B	1 per group
		18C	1 per group
graduated cylinder (25 mL)	S	8	1 per group
graduated cylinder (100 mL)	S	10B	1 per group
		11	1 per group (plastic)
		13A	1 per group
		13B	1 per group
		13C	1 per group
		16A (alt)	1 per group
		17A	1 per group
incandescent light	L	4A	1 per group
iron ring	S	1	1 per group
		2A	1 per group
		2B	1 per group
		6	1 per group
		8	1 per group
		9A	1 per group
		9B	1 per group
		9C	1 per group
		10A	1 per group
		11	1 per group
		12A	1 per group
		13A	1 per group
		13B	1 per group

Equipment	Source*	Lab	Notes
		16A	1 per group
		18B	1 per group
		18C	1 per group
laboratory apron	S	most	1 per person
M&M's, plain and peanut (or comparable)	L	4B	50 per group (must be two different types)
magnet	L	2B	1 per group
		2B (alt)	1 per group
magnifying glass	L	2B	1 per group
		2B (alt)	1 per group
marker, black	L	14	2–3 per class
		16B	2–3 per class
		19	2–3 per class
matches	L	many	1 box per group
melting point capillary tubes, at least 10 cm long	S	10A	2–3 per group
metal bar or cylinder	L or S	3B	1 per group
metric ruler, clear plastic (or meter stick)	L or S	3A	1 per group
		3B	1 per group
		5	1 per group
		10A	1 per group
		12A	1 per group
mortar and pestle	S	18C	1 per group
pennies	L	3A	10 per group
pH meter (optional)	S	16A	1 per 10 students
pH paper, wide range, pH 0–13 (optional)	S	16A	4 1-centimeter-long strips per group
pinchcock clamp	S	1	1 per group
		10B	1 per group
plastic wrap	L	11	1 1-inch square per group
		13B	1 1-inch square per group
polystyrene cups, 6–8 oz	L	13A	3 per group
		13B	2 per group
		13C	2 per group
reference source	L	20	1 per teacher (must have precise masses of atoms)
ring stand	S	1	1 per group
		2A	1 per group
		2B	1 per group
		6	1 per group
		8	1 per group
		9A	1 per group
		9B	1 per group
		9C	1 per group
		10A	1 per group
		10B	1 per group
		11	1 per group
		12A	1 per group
		13A	1 per group
		13B	1 per group
		13C	1 per group
		14	1 per group
		16A	1 per group
		16B	1 per group
		17A	1 per group
		18B	1 per group

Equipment	Source*	Lab	Notes
rubber bands, orthodontic	L	18C	1 per group
		10A	2 per group
rubber stopper	S	10B	1 #3 1-hole and 1 #6 2-hole per group
		12B	1 #00 1-hole, split, per group
		13B	1 #4 1-hole, split, per group
		15	1 #00 1-hole, split, per group
		18B	3 per group (to fit test tubes used)
sandpaper, 100–200 grit	L	9A	1 1-inch square per group
		13C	1 1-inch square per group
		17B	1 2-inch square per group
spatula	S	1	1 per group
		2B (alt)	1 per group
		9C	1 per group
		10B	1 per group
test tube brush	S	many	1 per group
test tube clamp	S	1	1 per group
		10A	1 per group
		10B	1 per group
		13C	1 per group
test tube holder	S	1	1 per group
		2B	1 per group
		12A	1 per group
		13B	1 per group
		15	1 per group
test tube, large (at least 18 × 150 mm)	S	1	2 per group
		10B	1 per group
		13B	1 per group
test tube rack	S	1	1 per group
		2B	1 per group
		2B (alt)	1 per group
		6	1 per group
		14	1 per group
		15	1 per group
		16A	1 per group
		16A (alt)	2 per group
		18B	1 per group
		18C	1 per group
test tubes	S	1	10 (13 × 100 mm) per group
		2B	4 per group
		2B (alt)	4 per group
		3A	1 per group
		6	6 per group
		9C	1 per group
		12A	4 per group
		12B	3 per group
		14	10 per group
		15	5 per group
		16A	8 per group
		16A (alt)	21 per group
		17B	4 per group
		18B	6 per group
		18C	12 per group
thermometer	S	10A	1 per group
		10B	1 per group
		11	1 per group
		12A	1 per group

Equipment	Source*	Lab	Notes
		12B	2 per group
		13A	1 per group
		13B	1 per group
		13C	1 per group
		14	1 per group
toothpicks	L	7	20 per group
		18A	80 per group
towels, paper or cloth	L	9A	1 per group
		13A	1–2 per group
		13C	1 per group
		17B	1 per group
transfer pipets, plastic (or eyedroppers)	S	1	3 per group
		2B	1 per group
		9A	1 per group
		9C	1 per group
		15	2 per group
		16A	1 per group
		16A (alt)	1 per group
		16B	1 per group
		18B	3 per group
		18C	1 per group
tubing, glass	S	10B	1 20-centimeter piece and 3 8-centimeter pieces per group
tubing, rubber	S	10B	2 45-centimeter pieces per group
wash bottle	S	1	1 per group (In addition to these labs, a wash bottle is useful for dispensing water in many other labs.)
		9C	1 per group
		16B	1 per group
watch glass, 60 mm	S	1	1 per group
watch glass, 150 mm	S	1	1 per group
		2A	1 per group
		9C	1 per group
		10A	1 per group
		16A	2 per group
watch with second hand	L	14	1 per group
weighing paper	S	2B	2–3 per group
		2B (alt)	2–3 per group
		6	3 per group
		9C	1–2 per group
		10B	2 per group
		13C	1–2 per group
wire gauze	S	1	1 per group
		2A	1 per group
		2B	1 per group
		6	1 per group
		9C	1 per group
		10A	1 per group
		11	1 per group
		12A	1 per group
		13A	2 per group
		13B	1 per group
		16A	1 per group
		18B	1 per group
		18C	1 per group
wooden splints	S	4A	7 per group